THE
NEW WORLD
OF MATHEMATICS

THE
NEW WORLD
OF MATHEMATICS

by GEORGE A. W. BOEHM
and the Editors of FORTUNE

Diagrams: Max Gschwind

FABER AND FABER
24 Russell Square
London

First published in England in mcmlx
by Faber and Faber Limited
24 Russell Square London WC1
Printed in Great Britain
by Lowe and Brydone (Printers) Ltd.
London NW10

CONTENTS

ERRATA

p. 15, l. 11 for 'Latta' read 'Lynn'.

p. 112, l. 8 for 'below' read 'on p. 111'.

p. 119, l. 17 from bottom, delete first figure 5 and the multiplication sign following.

p. 128, l. 5 for '1-2' read '2-3'.

PREFACE

Mathematics is for people who like to climb intellectual mountains. This book is intended to guide you into the foothills of mathematics, from where you can glimpse the towering peaks that keen minds have been discovering and conquering over the last five thousand years.

In all its long history mathematics has never been so lively a subject as it is today. In the last decade or two the pace of mathematical discovery and invention has accelerated amazingly. This book outlines some of the exciting work that mathematicians are now doing. The first two sections were published in Fortune in the summer of 1958. They deal with modern mathematics, pure and applied, and they delve into the nature of mathematicians. The third section also appeared in Fortune, in March, 1959. It takes up the future of computers as mathematical-logical machines. To these three articles has been added an appendix of nine short essays, which go deeper into some concepts and techniques of modern mathematics.

Probably the day has passed when an amateur could make important contributions to mathematics. The ideas are now so lofty and the techniques so intricate that only men with special aptitudes and training can create new mathematics. But almost any alert and persistent person can comprehend and enjoy the concepts of mathematics.

It is a pity that so few people today are given a chance to appreciate mathematics. Somehow the subject has been lost from the liberal-arts course, where historically it held a central position. Plato considered mathematics indispensable to the cultured man. In medieval times the quadrivium, the first postgraduate liberal-arts curriculum, consisted of arithmetic, geometry, astronomy, and music. And until recent times, leading universities required mathematics as part of the natural philosophy course.

Educators today seem to have lost sight of the fact that mathematics is an essential element in the cultural heritage of the Western world. When they teach the painting, the sculpture, the literature, and the philosophy of the Renaissance, they ignore the reawakening of mathematical thought that took place concurrently. It was at this time, for example, that mathematicians began pondering the nature of chance and developing the theory of probability that has enabled physicists, economists, statisticians, and social scientists to deal rationally with the basically uncertain world. When mathematics is taught, it is presented mainly as a collection of slightly related techniques and manipulations. The profound, yet simple, concepts get little attention. If art appreciation were taught in the same way, it would consist mostly of learning how to chip stone and mix paints.

To be sure, mathematics has a place in the vocational training of surveyors, engineers, statisticians, accountants, and scientists. But mathematics is also worth learning for its own sake—simply for intellectual thrill and stimulation. An increasing number of teachers are being equipped to teach the concepts of mathematics, particularly at the high-school level where young minds are wide open to fresh ideas. Today thousands of high-school teachers are returning to college for additional mathematical training under various fellowship programs. Perhaps the leaders of the next generation will understand mathematics as a universal language, even if they need never apply it.

Popular knowledge of mathematics is now appallingly scanty. Newspapers and magazines conscientiously report the latest developments in medicine, chemistry, physics, biology, and technology. Yet few publications ever discuss mathematics. Late in 1956, for example, two theoretical physicists, Chen Ning Yang and Tsung Dao Lee, demolished the principle of parity. The press did a commendable job of describing the abstruse physical ideas and the implications of Yang's and Lee's work. Significantly, however, nothing was said about the mathematics of group theory on which the two physicists based their conclusions. The reason is that there is no established popular terminology for talking *about* mathematics. Where physicists, with profound reservations, talk about atoms and subatomic particles as if they were tiny marbles, mathematicians generally talk only in mathematical terms. The public cannot understand and does not listen.

Communicating mathematical ideas is a problem even among mathematicians. Many leading mathematicians are distressed over a style of mathematical writing that has become commonplace in the last decade or two. Mathematical papers are compressed to the limit, until all intuitive ideas are squeezed out. As a result, one mathematician complains, "Most papers are read only three times—once by the author, once by the editor, and once by the reviewer."

Some mathematicians today fear that their subject is becoming almost a pure exercise in manipulating symbols. It is true that skill in symbolism can cover up and embellish trivial ideas. "There is less to this than meets the eye," is the comment that one leading mathematician applies to impressive-looking papers that are low on ideas. While he disparages only the content of the papers, other mathematicians are concerned about the soaring abstraction of their subject. They argue that while mathematics has always derived its most fertile inspirations from the physical world, most creative mathematicians today are getting completely out of touch with physical reality.

Symbolism offers rewards as well as peril. It is

difficult to see how most modern mathematical ideas could have been developed without the marvelously compact notation in use today. Throughout history, in fact, improvements in notation have closely paralleled progress in mathematics.

The way numbers were written in the Ancient World, only skilled technicians could do elementary arithmetic. The Egyptians, for example, used a clumsy decimal system more akin to Roman numerals than to modern numbers. The Egyptian scribe represented 1 by a straight line; for 9 he drew nine lines. He represented 10 by an inverted U; for 99 he had to draw nine inverted U's and nine straight lines. All fractions had 1 as a numerator; 7/29 had to be written as the sum of 1/6, 1/24, 1/58, 1/87, and 1/232. There were lengthy tables for representing fractions as the sum of other fractions. The Babylonians used an even more cumbersome number system that was not decimal but based on the number 60—i.e., there were 60 different digit symbols. Yet somehow the Egyptians managed to develop surveying and Babylonian astronomers calculated rather accurately the value of π.

Even the Greeks, who made so many contributions to mathematics, were also handicapped by a number system that was extremely hard to handle. Nonetheless, the Pythagoreans discerned and proved that numbers like $\sqrt{2}$ were irrational (i.e., not expressible as fractions), and Euclid demonstrated that the number of prime numbers is infinite. Archimedes, a Sicilian of Greek extraction, even invented and applied a primitive form of integral calculus.

The Greeks were, however, mainly interested in geometry. It was during the Dark Ages, while mathematics in Europe and Egypt stagnated, that the Hindus developed algebra. They were helped by a vastly improved notation. They invented the numbers we now call arabic, but their most important contribution was positional notation. Instead of representing 99 by the symbol for 10 repeated nine times and the symbol for 1 repeated nine times, the Hindus wrote it pretty much as we do today. They also started using special symbols to represent unknown quantities.

During the Renaissance the geometry of the West began to blend with the algebra of the East. The mixing was finally completed early in the seventeenth century in France, when René Descartes devised analytic geometry, a way of representing geometric figures as algebraic equations, and vice versa. It was around Descartes' time that European mathematicians finally settled on modern symbolism—e.g., the ways of writing cube roots, exponents, and equality, and representing constants by the first letters of the alphabet and variables by the last letters. Until that time mathematicians had had to communicate their ideas largely by expressing them rhetorically—e.g., for $4x^5$, "the product of the cube of an unknown quantity by its square and the number four." Thought processes being largely symbolic, it is remarkable that mathematicians had been able to think coherently without streamlined notation. It is doubtful whether today's mathematicians, without a symbolic short-hand, could make any progress.

Taken together, the parts of this book survey most of modern mathematics. For those who want to dig deeper, the following is a representative, though certainly not exhaustive, list of the good books that have been written about mathematics:

What Is Mathematics? by Richard Courant and Herbert Robbins, Oxford University Press. Two leading mathematicians discuss at length many of the important ideas and methods of mathematics.

Mathematics and the Imagination by Edward Kasner and James Newman, Bell & Sons Ltd. A clear and often amusing account of some vital concepts.

Prelude to Mathematics by W. W. Sawyer, Penguin Books. One of the clearest and cleverest writers in the mathematical brotherhood describes some of the aspects of algebra and geometry that he finds exciting.

Introduction to Finite Mathematics by John G. Kemeny, J. Laurie Snell, and Gerald L. Thompson, Bailey Bros. & Swinfen Ltd. Three members of the young and vigorous Dartmouth College mathematics department present some really modern aspects of mathematics as a readable elementary textbook.

An Introduction to Probability Theory and Its Applications by William Feller, Chapman & Hall Ltd. A beautifully written college textbook that is rough going for the unmathematical, but well worth reading by those not afraid of algebraic symbols.

The World of Mathematics (four volumes) edited by James Newman, Simon & Schuster. The best-selling survey of mathematics from early Egypt till now. Even if some of the articles are fairly technical, the editor's introductory paragraphs are probably worth the price of the books.

How to Solve It by George Pólya, Oxford University Press. An eminent mathematician tells how he solves problems and suggests how you can.

A Mathematician's Apology by G. H. Hardy, Cambridge University Press. An introspective account by one of the world's great pure mathematicians of how and why men like himself create new mathematical ideas.

Much of the credit for this book belongs to Betty Fullen, one of FORTUNE's expert researchers, who developed a profound understanding of mathematicians, despite their efforts to bewilder her by writing rapidly on blackboards. The diagrams are by Max Gschwind of the FORTUNE Art Department, who took the time and trouble to understand the subject matter before starting to draw.

The editors of FORTUNE would also like to express their deep appreciation to the many mathematicians, logicians, and computer experts who spent hours at a stretch explaining their ideas of what is important and exciting in modern mathematics. To those who made the additional effort of reviewing the rough drafts of the manuscripts, correcting errors, and suggesting how some ideas could be explained better, special thanks. Their names are listed below:

AMERICAN MATHEMATICAL SOCIETY: J. H. Curtiss.

CALIFORNIA INSTITUTE OF TECHNOLOGY: H. Frederic Bohnenblust, C. R. DePrima, Robert P. Dilworth, John Todd.

COLUMBIA UNIVERSITY: Samuel Eilenberg, Herbert Robbins.

CORNELL UNIVERSITY: Mark Kac, Frank Rosenblatt, J. Barkley Rosser, Balthasar van der Pol.

DARTMOUTH COLLEGE: John G. Kemeny, J. Laurie Snell.

HARVARD UNIVERSITY: Andrew M. Gleason, Latta H. Loomis, George W. Mackey, Willard V. Quine, J. L. Walsh, Oscar Zariski.

ILLINOIS INSTITUTE OF TECHNOLOGY: Karl Menger.

INDIANA UNIVERSITY: J. W. T. Youngs.

INSTITUTE FOR ADVANCED STUDY: Deane Montgomery, Marston Morse.

INTERNATIONAL BUSINESS MACHINES CORPORATION: John W. Backus, Robert W. Bemer, Roy Goldfinger, John Greenstadt, Louis Robinson, Irving Ziller.

LOS ALAMOS SCIENTIFIC LABORATORY: Stanislaw M. Ulam.

MASSACHUSETTS INSTITUTE OF TECHNOLOGY: William N. Locke, William Ted Martin, John McCarthy, John Nash, Hartley Rogers Jr., Claude E. Shannon, Victor H. Yngve.

NATIONAL BUREAU OF STANDARDS: Alan L. Leiner, Ida Rhodes.

NEW YORK UNIVERSITY: Lipman Bers, Richard Courant.

OFFICE OF NAVAL RESEARCH: Arthur Grad, Ivar Stakgold, F. Joachim Weyl.

PRINCETON UNIVERSITY: Emil Artin, William Feller, Carl G. Hempel, Solomon Lefschetz, D. C. Spencer, N. E. Steenrod, A. W. Tucker, John W. Tukey, Eugene Wigner, Samuel S. Wilks.

RAND CORPORATION: Paul Armer, Richard Bellman, George B. Dantzig, Murray A. Geisler, Kenneth Harper, J. C. Shaw, Philip Wolfe.

REMINGTON RAND (Div. of Sperry Rand Corporation): William Finley, Grace Murray Hopper, Donald Klick, James R. Weiner.

RESEARCH INSTITUTE FOR ADVANCED STUDY, INC.: Robert W. Bass, Welcome W. Bender, Solomon Schwartzman.

SHELL DEVELOPMENT COMPANY: Harold Gershinowitz.

STANFORD UNIVERSITY: George Pólya.

UNIVERSITY OF CALIFORNIA: (Berkeley) Edward W. Barankin, David Blackwell, Bernard Friedman, D. H. Lehmer, Hans Lewy, Charles B. Morrey Jr., Alfred Tarski, Frantisek Wolf.

(Livermore) Joseph L. Brady, Sidney Fernbach.

UNIVERSITY OF CHICAGO: A. Adrian Albert, Irving Kaplansky, Saunders MacLane, Nicolas Rashevsky, Irving E. Segal, Edwin H. Spanier, Marshall H. Stone.

UNIVERSITY OF ILLINOIS: Max Beberman.

G.A.W.B.

1

THE NEW MATHEMATICS

Today the fastest-growing and most radically changing of all the sciences is mathematics. It is the only
branch of learning in which all the major theories of
two thousand years ago are still valid, yet never before has there been such a flood of fresh ideas. New
branches of mathematics, like game theory, are beginning to yield remarkable insights into human relationships that scientists have never before analyzed
precisely. Old branches, like probability theory, are
being applied to such fresh areas as traffic flow and
communication. And space flight challenges mathematicians to invent new navigational techniques far
more complex than those that now guide ships and
airplanes.

In the last decade the number of U.S. mathematicians has doubled; today the National Science
Foundation's roster of scientists and technicians lists
20,000 people who make their living with mathemat-

ics. Enrollments in advanced mathematics courses are rising fast—by 30 per cent a year in some universities. Demand, of course, has been soaring. Industry and the government are beginning to hire some of the best mathematicians. Taking advantage of the speed of electronic computers, the mathematicians are solving a steadily widening range of practical problems in economics as well as technology.

But it is not in the practical application of mathematics that the greatest changes are taking place. At the very time when people are seeing more and more utility in mathematics, the leading theoretical mathematicians are moving pure mathematics further away from the physical world. Mathematicians have always been partial to abstraction, and for its own sake— aesthetics, not usefulness, is their criterion. Yet today they are moving to heights of abstraction their forebears hardly dared contemplate. They conceive some geometries of an infinite number of dimensions and others where size is meaningless. They develop algebras that transcend the familiar rules of arithmetic. They explore universal abstract patterns that link such disparate concepts as numbers, spaces, motions, and algebraic formulas.

Out of all this may well come one of the most exciting intellectual adventures in history. The time lag may be a long one, but mathematical developments of the most abstract nature—seemingly useless, even frivolous—have ultimately inspired the creation of new theories in the other sciences. Back in 1854, for example, the German Bernhard Riemann invented a non-Euclidean geometry. It remained in the realm of pure mathematics until, a half century later, Albert Einstein used it as a basis for relativity theory, and from relativity theory, of course, flowed modern physics. The abstractions that mathematicians are creating today will almost certainly, many years from now, open the way to new theories as far reaching as relativity—and perhaps even whole new branches of science.

And mathematics is one field of pure research in which Americans excel. Europeans, with justice, complain that U.S. science has been too pragmatic, too much concerned with experimental techniques, expensive machines, and elaborate instruments. U.S. mathematicians have, however, consistently leaned in the other direction—and with remarkable success. There are surprisingly few creative pure mathematicians—not more than 3,000 in the whole world. But the 600 in this country rank with the best anywhere.

To these men mathematics is almost like a game. They no longer rely on intuition developed by experience with the physical world. Instead they define their own world by axioms. Unlike the axioms of Euclid, which were derived from observation and supposed to be "self-evident truths," those of modern mathematics are admittedly abstract assumptions. In a narrow sense, they are no more "true" than the rules of chess. But they are by no means entirely arbitrary. For while pure mathematicians have pushed their abstractions beyond the physical world, they are responsible to mathematical "reality"—a sort of Platonic ideal that raises mathematics far above the level of a mere game—and a skillful mathematician chooses his axioms to reveal that peculiar reality. Yet mathematicians can never be sure that what they create is logically perfect. For it is beyond the powers of mathematics to prove its own consistency.

Many of the basic concepts are inherently simple —so simple, indeed, that a child can understand them. Some of the most difficult problems in modern mathematics have arisen from the theory of infinite sets—i.e., collections of an infinite number of things, such as all the points on a line or all the conceivable whole numbers. Yet the late Edward Kasner of Columbia University used to lecture on infinite sets to kindergarten classes. The children, he found, readily reconciled themselves to the notion of infinity and got the fundamental ideas of set theory faster than some of his undergraduate students. Children seem to be naturally attuned to mathematical abstraction, perhaps because it is not unlike pure fantasy. (It may be significant that one of the best-loved children's books, *Alice's Adventures in Wonderland,* was written by a professional mathematician, Charles Lutwidge Dodgson; pen name, Lewis Carroll.)

The elegance of ideas

One of the highest compliments one mathematician can pay another's work is to call it "elegant," for if one thing sets pure mathematics apart from all other sciences, it is the aesthetic standard mathematicians apply to their subject. Elegant mathematics is as hard to define as a pretty girl. But Professor George Pólya of Stanford University has stated one definition of mathematical elegance that many mathematicians accept. In his opinion, the elegance of a theorem is "directly proportional to the number of ideas you can see in it and inversely proportional to the effort it takes to see them."

A famous British mathematician, the late G. H. Hardy, dug deeper into the subject in a readable little book entitled *A Mathematician's Apology*. He wrote: "The mathematician's patterns, like the painter's or the poet's, must be *beautiful;* the ideas, like the colors or the words, must fit together in a harmonious way ... there is no permanent place in the world for ugly mathematics." Hardy also perceived a functional quality in mathematical beauty. An elegant mathematical idea, unlike a crossword puzzle or a chess problem, cannot be an intellectual dead end; it must link other mathematical ideas and thus enrich mathematics.

One of the most eminent U.S. mathematicians, Marston Morse of the Institute for Advanced Study, goes a step further. "The first essential bond between mathematics and the arts," he says, "is found in the fact that discovery in mathematics is not a matter of logic. It is rather the result of mysterious powers which no one understands, and in which the unconscious recognition of beauty must play an important part. Out of an infinity of designs a mathematician chooses one pattern for beauty's sake, and pulls it down to earth."

The pure mathematician's highly developed sense of aesthetics seems to carry over to one of the arts: music. Quite a number of mathematicians are excellent instrumentalists, and many mathematical centers have organized chamber-music groups, even small orchestras. In music, by all odds the most abstract of the arts, mathematicians see a clear reflection of many of their own concepts. It is even possible for them to analyze, mathematically, the peculiarities of style that distinguish composers. A computer has, indeed, been successfully programed to compose music in the style of Bach.

Many mathematicians play such games as chess, bridge, or the Oriental board game Go. But, curiously, few excel at them (although two former world's chess champions, Emanuel Lasker and Max Euwe, and two of the best U.S. bridge players, were trained in mathematics). While creating mathematics and playing games may require the same kind of thinking, the pace is different. In his work a mathematician can correct his errors upon reflection; in a game he must commit himself quickly and irrevocably, and mathematicians are not exceptionally good at snap decisions.

A few mathematicians have exceptional spatial visualization and computational skill. Some have an intuitive feeling for the relationship, for example, between a five-dimensional object and a seven-dimensional space that surrounds it. And the late John von Neumann of the Institute for Advanced Study used to astound other mathematicians with his speed in solving long and complicated probems in his head.

As a rule, however, mathematicians probably cannot visualize ordinary shapes as clearly as engineers and mechanics, nor can they do arithmetic as rapidly as accountants.

The one attribute that virtually all creative mathematicians share is youth. Isaac Newton, for example, said he was at the peak of his mathematical power at the age of twenty-three and twenty-four. Most great mathematicians have made their major contributions by the time they were thirty or forty. After fifty they have generally concentrated on teaching or philosophy or the application of mathematics to other fields.

But perhaps the outstanding characteristic of mathematicians is that they like to do their own work. Group research does not attract them. Relatively few research papers in mathematics have more than one author, and almost none have more than two. Nor do mathematicians need much equipment besides a private office, reference library, and paper and pencils. While physicists and chemists are tied down to instruments and machines, mathematicians are free to roam. They roam a great deal—much more than scientists in other fields. It is not uncommon for a mathematician to travel halfway around the world to exchange ideas with another mathematician.

THE "GROUP" CONCEPT: A WAY OF
The basic notion

Perhaps the most versatile abstraction of modern mathematics is the algebraic concept of "group." A group helps unify the many branches of mathematics, for it applies equally to the basic structures of spaces, numbers, motions, formulas, and other mathematical objects. Like most useful mathematical abstractions, groups are very simple in principle—very complicated in application.

Every group is defined by a table similar to a multiplication table. A group table consists of a number of elements (represented in the tables below by letters) and a rule for combining the elements. The diagram and first two tables illustrate a relatively simple group of operations. They move a square without altering the appearance of its outline although they may change the location of specific corners. The square can be considered a piece of cardboard resting on the page. The operations are equivalent to interchanging in various ways the letters at the corners. The commutative law does not apply to this group, i.e., the order in which the operations are carried out can make a difference. Operation F (on vertical scale) followed by operation A (on horizontal scale) interchanges corner M with corner N and corner P with corner Q; the result is therefore equivalent to operation E. On the other hand, operation A followed by operation F

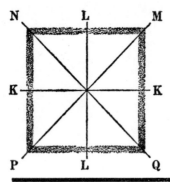

I	identity, don't move square
A	rotate square 90° counter clockwise
B	rotate square 180° counter clockwise
C	rotate square 270° counter clockwise
D	flip over square around axis K–K
E	flip over square around axis L–L
F	flip over square around axis M–P
G	flip over square around axis N–Q

SEEING THE SKELETON OF MATHEMATICS

interchanges *N* with *P* and *M* with *Q* and the result is equivalent to operation *D*. (The axes don't move when the square is rotated or flipped.)

The smaller group table (below, right) represents three different mathematical processes and reveals, thereby, that they all have the same fine filigree of mathematical structure. (It is a commutative group, for the operations can be made in any order.) The table can be interpreted in any of the following ways:

(1) The rotations that do not alter the outline of a square. *I*, the identity element, does not move the square. *A* rotates it 90° counter-clockwise; *B*, 180°; and *C*, 270°. (A "subgroup" of the group represented by the large table.)

(2) Additions in a number system consisting of only four numbers: 0, 1, 2, and 3. This is equivalent to adding whole numbers, dividing the sum by four, and writing down the remainder. In this interpretation the identity *I* is zero; *A* is 1; *B* is 2; and *C* is 3.

(3) Multiplications in a number system consisting of the numbers 1, 2, 3, and 4. This is equivalent to multiplying the whole numbers, dividing by five, and writing down the remainder. The identity *I* is 1; *A* is 2; *B* is 4; and *C* is 3.

	I	A	B	C	D	E	F	G
I	I	A	B	C	D	E	F	G
A	A	B	C	I	G	F	D	E
B	B	C	I	A	E	D	G	F
C	C	I	A	B	F	G	E	D
D	D	F	E	G	I	B	A	C
E	E	G	D	F	B	I	C	A
F	F	E	G	D	C	A	I	B
G	G	D	F	E	A	C	B	I

	I	A	B	C
I	I	A	B	C
A	A	B	C	I
B	B	C	I	A
C	C	I	A	B

A challenging problem

One important application of group theory is in the field of topology—a kind of geometry that studies general relationships of form and space with no regard to size. The problem is to calculate "homotopy" groups of spheres. It amounts roughly to this: In how many ways can you wrap a rubber sphere around another sphere?

It must first be understood that "sphere" in this context stands for an infinite variety of geometric objects of different dimensions. A one-dimensional sphere, S^1, is a circle. A two-dimensional sphere, S^2, is a hollow ball. Spheres of higher dimensions are, of course, impossible to represent in the physical world; they are mathematical extensions of the concept of perfect roundness. Geometrically, the process of building a sphere of one higher dimension than a given sphere consists of choosing two points (poles) in the next dimension and joining them to every point on the given sphere. Algebraically, a sphere of n dimensions is represented by the following equation:

$$X_1^2 + X_2^2 + X_3^2 + \cdots + X_n^2 + X_{n+1}^2 = 1$$

Each X stands for the distance in a different dimension from a point on the outside of the sphere to the center.

The problem is all the more challenging for being half solved. Some of the cases are relatively simple. A circle can be wrapped around another circle in infinitely many ways: once around, twice around, three times around, etc. Like this:

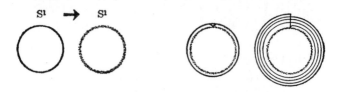

But there is basically only one way to wrap a circle around a hollow ball. Since the circle is like a rubber band, it can be slid off the equator of the ball and shrunk to a single point, like this:

Wrapping one hollow ball around another is similar to wrapping one circle around another circle. The outer ball can be slit and wrapped around the inner one any number of times. On the other hand, a hollow ball squeezed to a line and wrapped around a circle can always be shrunk down to a single point, like this:

It is generally true that if the two spheres have the same dimension, one can be wrapped around the other an infinite number of ways. And the outer sphere can always be shrunk to a point if it has fewer dimensions than the inner sphere.

The most interesting cases are those in which the outer sphere has more dimensions than the inner sphere. With purely algebraic methods developed by the French mathematician Jean Leray and first applied to homotopy groups in 1950 by another French mathematician, Jean-Pierre Serre, it is theoretically possible to calculate the number of ways any given sphere can be wrapped around any other given sphere. But the computation is so enormously difficult and tedious

Dimensions of outer sphere	of inner sphere	Number of ways of wrapping
3	2	infinite
4	3	2
4	2	2
5	3	2
17	3	30
18	4	90,720
19	5	12
26	11	480
27	12	480
31	16	infinite

that algebraic topologists are still seeking a general rule. Several dozen cases have already been calculated, most of them by a Japanese mathematician, Hirosi Toda. The table above lists some of the results. Frustratingly irregular, they fail to reveal a definite mathematical pattern of the kind that algebraic topologists hope to find.

Yet good mathematicians thrive in a community of scholars. The bulk of the best pure mathematics is produced at a few centers where outstanding mathematicians have attracted other good mathematicians and the best students. Just which are the greatest centers is debatable, but any list would have to include: Chicago, Harvard, and Princeton University, as well as the Institute for Advanced Study at Princeton, and abroad, Leningrad, Moscow, and Paris.

Good questions

Among professional mathematicians, asking questions rates almost as high as answering them. Mathematics abounds with problems that have remained unsolved for decades or even centuries and yet have stimulated whole new branches of the science. Mathematicians have, for example, developed much of the modern theory of numbers during attempts to check a conjecture of an otherwise obscure German amateur named Goldbach. In 1742 he said that every even number greater than two is the sum of two prime numbers (a prime being a number that is not exactly divisible by any other whole number except one). For instance: 8 is equal to 3 plus 5; 26 is equal to 13 plus 13; and 62 is equal to 3 plus 59. No one has yet found a mathematical proof for Goldbach's assertion, but on the other hand no one has found an exception that would disprove it. The problem has, however, been whittled down. In 1931 a Russian mathematician named Schnirelmann proved that every positive number is the sum of not more than 300,000 prime numbers. Then another Russian, Vinogradov, showed that every sufficiently large odd number is the sum of not more than three primes. But what is "sufficiently large"? Now it is known that "sufficiently large" means at least 350,000 digits—a number that would fill fifteen to twenty pages of a metropolitan telephone directory. There the question rests.

The greatest single feat of problem posing was that of the great German mathematician David Hilbert. In 1900 he stated no less than twenty-three problems and challenged his fellow mathematicians to solve them in the new century. For years mathematicians used the status of the Hilbert problems as a barometer of progress. Most have now been solved, but as late as 1952 there was a furor when Hilbert's fifth problem was solved by three U.S. mathematicians: Andrew Gleason of Harvard, Deane Montgomery of the Institute for Advanced Study, and Leo Zippin of Queens College. And just last year a leading Russian mathematician, A. N. Kolmogorov, published a proof of the thirteenth. (Like most of Hilbert's problems, the fifth and the thirteenth are extremely technical.)

The knack of posing good problems is intimately related to a kind of unfettered guesswork that mathematicians use to create mathematics. Mathematics in the making, as Pólya points out, is not a deductive science; it is an inductive, experimental science, and guessing is the experimental tool of mathematics. Mathematicians, like other scientists, formulate their theories from hunches, analogies, and simple examples. They work out their rigorous proofs only after they are pretty confident that what they are trying to prove is indeed correct.

Pólya contends that shrewd guessing can and should be taught. He has written three books on the subject, including a lively paper-back volume, *How to Solve It*. Plausible reasoning has logical rules of its own, he says, and among the examples he gives are the following:

If A implies B,
and if B is quite probable in itself,
and if B turns out to be true,
then A becomes just a little more credible.

If A implies B,
and if B is very improbable in itself,
and if, nevertheless, B turns out to be true,
then A becomes very much more credible.

Such reasoning obviously falls far short of incontrovertible proof, but it can help guide a mathematician to an idea that is worth trying to prove.

Mathematical *proof*, however, demands an entirely different kind of reasoning. When he comes to write up the results of his research, the mathematician puts aside the shrewd hunch, the illuminating analogy, and the other tools of invention and uses only the bulldozer of logical deduction. In a formal proof he can leave nothing to the imagination. He must start out with all necessary definitions and axioms and inexorably grind out a conclusion without making further assumptions.

Strictly speaking, the careful mathematician cannot say: "Such and such is true." He must instead make statements like: "If A is true, then B is true." And he must realize, moreover, that the truth of his statements is relative only to mathematics and has no direct bearing on the physical world. It is this formalism that led Bertrand Russell to define mathematics as "the subject in which we never know what we are talking about, nor whether what we are saying is true."

Monsieur Bourbaki

The most ambitious movement in mathematical formalism started out as a joke and still has elements of a joke. It consists of the writings of a wholly fictitious Frenchman, Nicolas Bourbaki, and it is perhaps the only large-scale collaborative effort in modern mathematics. To date he has published some twenty volumes, totaling over 3,000 pages.

Bourbaki was born some twenty-five years ago in the whimsical imagination of a group of young French mathematicians led by André Weil, one of the greatest living mathematicians. Bourbaki started by writing brief technical notes to the journals. Then about 1940 he set himself an imposing task: to compile a complete and logically rigorous exposition of all mathematics.

Bourbaki is an eccentric. He uses his own peculiar notation; when his reasoning is about to take a dangerous turn, for example, he warns his readers by drawing in the margin a zigzag that looks like a French road sign.

Co-founder Weil retired recently from Bourbaki (though not from mathematics) when he reached the age of fifty. Bourbaki, however, has no intention of retiring. He will presumably remain young and active forever, or at least as long as mathematicians keep creating new concepts and techniques. Some of the members believe that Bourbaki's stupendous exposition (called simply *The Elements of Mathematics*) will need periodic rewriting. The first volumes, they say, are already obsolescent, so fast has mathematics progressed in the last few years.

While Bourbaki's approach to mathematics is ultramethodical, all mathematicians reason cautiously —and with good reason. Plausible but unproved assumptions have in the past led to too many paradoxes. Some of the great mathematicians of the last century ran into serious trouble when they assumed that in certain infinite sets there was necessarily a greatest or a least thing. It isn't so. While the following example is so simple that it could not lead a mathematician astray, it illustrates, nevertheless, some of the logical complexity of infinite sets. There are an infinite number of common fractions, for example, but there is no smallest fraction. Given any small fraction (e.g., 1/999,999), it is always possible to find a smaller one simply by adding one to the denominator (e.g., 1/1,000,000).

The mathematical nature of infinite sets often shocks ordinary intuition. One of the most startling examples was described about twenty-five years ago by two Polish mathematicians, Stefan Banach and Alfred Tarski (the latter now a professor at the University of California). They pointed out how a solid sphere the size of a pea could, in theory, be divided into a finite number of pieces and then reassembled into a sphere the size of the sun.

Zorn's lemma

To chart a safe course through the perils of the infinite, mathematicians have had to devise new reasoning tools. One of the most valuable is a rule expressed in various forms and known by several names, including the "axiom of choice" and "Zorn's lemma." It concerns what mathematicians call "partially ordered" sets. A simple example would be the chain of command of the U. S. Army. An "ordered" (i.e., unbroken) line of authority passes down from the President to the commander of a regiment and ultimately to a private in that regiment. But there is no direct line of authority between, say, two lieutenants in different regiments. A more complicated partially ordered set is shown in this diagram:

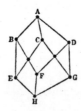

A given point is, by definition, greater than any other point to which it is connected by descending lines. (The lengths of the lines are not significant.) Thus A is greater than all the others; B is greater than E; C is greater than G; and all other points are greater than H. But the diagram is utterly noncommittal about the relationships among B, C, and D, or among E, F, and G.

Zorn's lemma states that in any partially ordered set there exists a maximal ordered set: that is, a direct chain of command that is not part of any other chain of command in the whole set. A maximal chain can

be easily picked out from the set in the diagram—
A, C, F, H, for instance. But from sets that consist of
thousands of points, or even infinitely many, it may
be humanly impossible to trace a maximal ordered
set. What Zorn's lemma does is to assure the mathematician that he can safely assume there exists a maximal ordered set in any partially ordered set he en-
counters. And with this assumption he can get on
with whatever he is trying to prove.

The intuitionists

Not all mathematicians agree that a set theory
which includes Zorn's lemma is logically valid. There
is a small but adamant minority, called "intuitionists,"
who want to rule out all propositions that merely
state the existence of a number or a formula or a set
without specifying it. If there is a maximal set, they
say, point it out or tell how to find it in a finite number of steps.

They also refuse to accept the indirect method
of proof. With this time-honored device, a mathematician who wishes to prove that a theorem is true
first assumes that it is false. He then proceeds to
reason to an absurd contradiction, and thereby con-
cludes that the theorem must be true. Indirect proofs,
the intuitionists point out, depend on Aristotle's law
of the excluded middle, which holds that statements
are logically either absolutely true or absolutely false,
never in between. And this law sometimes springs
logical leaks when it is applied to infinite sets.

Soon after the turn of the century David Hilbert

tried to shore up the foundations of mathematical logic. Taking a different tack from the intuitionists, he attempted to salvage classical reasoning by redefining mathematics as a game played according to certain explicit rules (or axioms) with meaningless symbols. His goal was to make mathematics self-contained and internally consistent; he seemed for a time to be on the verge of attaining it.

Then in 1931 Hilbert's whole logical structure was suddenly demolished. A young Austrian logician, Kurt Godel (now a professor at the Institute for Advanced Study at Princeton), showed that there was no hope of making mathematics internally perfect. Through a long and impeccable chain of reasoning Gödel analyzed all possible formal logical systems for defining mathematics. He showed that any system broad enough to include a definition of the whole numbers inevitably had to have two terrible flaws. First, it could not deduce all the elementary and intuitively obvious theorems of arithmetic. And worse yet, it could not prove its own logical consistency. Hilbert's system, in short, was beyond repair. Indeed, Hilbert himself was among the first to realize that Gödel's proof was incontrovertible. He abandoned his project, calling it a "fiasco."

While his great effort ended in futility, Hilbert has apparently emerged the winner in the conflict of mathematical logic. The vast majority of mathematicians are willing to accept his approach, risky though they know it to be. Harvard Professor Andrew Gleason explains this attitude: "If you take the intuitionist position, you are safe. But you can prove hardly anything with their restricted reasoning. We want to make progress; so we go ahead using the same old unsafe logic. We haven't yet run into a major paradox, although we can't be sure we won't someday. The Banach-Tarski discovery isn't really a paradox. That is, it's not a logical contradiction; it just shows we cannot have a completely general notion of volume. But if we do run into a paradox, we can probably save the structure of mathematics by patching it."

Algebra unlimited

Hilbert's detached axiomatic approach now permeates all of mathematics. In algebra, particularly, it has given mathematicians a degree of freedom that they never before enjoyed.

Algebraists used to confine themselves to what they could observe about the behavior of ordinary numbers. The Hindus modeled the original rules of algebra on the arithmetic of "rational" numbers— i.e., whole numbers and fractions. As luck would have it, the next two kinds of numbers to be admitted to mathematics did not require a change in the rules. First came the "irrational" numbers, like $\sqrt{3}$ or $\sqrt[3]{7}$, which are not exactly equal to any fractions, although they can be approximated by fractions. (The rational and irrational numbers together are called "real" numbers.)

Next came the "imaginary" number $\sqrt{-1}$. It is not even approximately equal to any real number, for there can be no real number whose square is a negative number. Yet the imaginary number, usually written as i, blends smoothly into the arithmetic of real numbers. Through addition, subtraction, multiplication, and division it combines with real numbers to form "complex" numbers—e.g., $3i$, $7 - \frac{1}{4}i$, $1\frac{1}{2} + \sqrt{3}\,i$. And complex numbers such as these can be added, subtracted, multiplied, and divided according to the rules that apply to real numbers.

Changing the rules

Not until the nineteenth century would mathematicians consider numbers that did not follow the old, familiar rules of arithmetic. Today, however, algebraists approach their subject from the other side. They start with the rules and modify them, often arbitrarily, to create new algebraic systems that do not apply to real or complex numbers. There are, theoretically, an unlimited number of such systems. It has been proved, however, that no numbers beyond the complex numbers (one real and one imaginary part) will obey all the old rules.

Every school child discovers sooner or later that if he has to multiply together a string of numbers, it makes no difference in what order he does the multiplication. But it makes a big difference in some types of numbers beyond the complex numbers. The most familiar of these are the quaternions, which have one real part and three different imaginaries. For quaternions the commutative law of multiplication breaks down; that is, if a and b are two quaternions, $a \times b$ is not necessarily equal to $b \times a$. For Cayley numbers (one real part and seven imaginaries) an even more drastic change takes place: the associative law of multiplication no longer holds true. That is to say, if *a*, *b*, and *c* are three Cayley numbers, you get one answer if you first multiply *a* by *b* and then multiply the result by *c*, and you get another answer if you first multiply *b* by *c* and multiply *a* by that result.

Another simple fact of arithmetic is that two numbers multiplied together equal zero only if at least one of the numbers actually is zero. This rule is true for quaternions and Cayley numbers. But beyond them it breaks down, and as a consequence there is no unique way of dividing numbers. This theorem was proved just a few months ago by Raoul Bott of Michigan, Michel Kervaire of the Institute for Advanced Study, and John Milnor of Princeton. Incidentally, they used every resource of algebraic topology, an abstract kind of geometry (defined below).

The grin remains

Modern mathematicians inherited one of the pivotal concepts of modern algebra: the "group." A brilliant young French mathematician, Evariste Galois, first used the group idea in 1830 to explore ways of solving equations. He wrote up his discovery on the eve of a duel in which he was killed at the age of twenty. Only in recent years have mathematicians fully exploited the group concept; it has emerged as a versatile tool for revealing the fine filigrees of logical structure that are common to many mathematical ideas.

A group has been compared to the grin that remains when Lewis Carroll's Cheshire cat fades away. It applies to all sorts of mathematical objects: physical motions, numbers, vectors, geometric spaces, and equations. Axiomatically, a group consists of a number of "elements" (mathematical objects of any sort) and a way of combining them. Some groups have an infinite number of elements. Representing the elements by letters and the combining process by the symbol $\star$, the axioms are as follows:

(1) All combinations of elements are themselves elements in the group.

(2) $a \star (b \star c) = (a \star b) \star c$, where it is understood that the combinations inside the parentheses are made first.

(3) There is an element, I (called the identity), such that $I \star a = a = a \star I$ for every element, a.

(4) For every element a there is an inverse: another element A such that $a \star A = I = A \star a$.

The elements, for example, might be all the positive whole numbers and fractions and the combining process might be multiplication. In that case, the identity element, the one that does not change the other elements when combined with them, would be the number 1. And the inverse of 2 would be ½. Or, the elements might be all the whole numbers, negative as well as positive, and the combining process might be addition. Then the identity element would have to be the number zero. And the inverse of 3 would be -3. In these two groups the commutative law holds; i.e., $a \star b$ invariably equals $b \star a$. But not all groups are commutative. A simple example is the group of motions in a dance. You arrive at one place if you first turn to your right and then walk three steps forward, but at an entirely different place if you first walk three steps forward and then turn to your right. (For more illustrations of groups, see diagrams on pages 24 and 25.)

Generalized geometries

Modern geometry is no less abstract than algebra. One of the most active branches of mathematics today is topology, a form of geometry based on a general notion of shape and a total disregard for size. For many purposes a topologist does not distinguish between a cube and a sphere or between an oval and a triangle. But he does see a basic difference between a sphere and any solid with a hole through it, e.g., a ring. And in his view all solids pierced by only one hole are alike (which leads other mathematicians to define a topologist as "a man who can't tell the difference between a doughnut and a cup of coffee").

One of the most fascinating results of topology is the fixed-point theorem found half a century ago by a Dutch mathematician, L. E. J. Brouwer. It states that if a solid disk is continuously deformed—i.e., stretched, shrunk, folded, or turned, but *not* torn— and then replaced within its original outlines, at least one point will end in the position where it started. If, for instance, the disk is simply rotated, the center point remains fixed. It is easier to appreciate the theorem if you think of the disk as a thin circular sheet of rubber or a platter covered with modeling clay. The theorem has been widely applied to other branches of mathematics including some as remote as hydrodynamics and game theory. (An odd note: the fixed-point theorem is a typical "existence" theorem, for it does not tell which point remains fixed. The intuitionists abhor existence theorems; yet Brouwer, having changed his outlook, has become the leader of the intuitionist school of mathematical logic.)

Algebra of shape

One of the most exciting and abstract fields of modern mathematics has arisen from a marriage of algebra and topology, namely, algebraic topology. The problems in it are typically geometric, but mathematicians use algebraic techniques to solve them. (For an example of a major problem in this field, see pages 26-28.)

Geometry has been generalized in other directions. Algebraic geometry, a theory rooted in the elementary subject taught as analytic geometry, makes free with all the abstract kinds of numbers that algebra can devise. It extends from the study of the elementary algebraic curves, or graphs, of analytic geometry to the general concept of algebraic curves and surfaces of any dimension.

Whereas mathematicians in the last century took a big step in exploring four-dimensional geometry, today they put no limit on the number of dimensions. Many do work on Hilbert space, a geometry of an infinite number of dimensions, in which distances and angles are measured much as they are in ordinary

Euclidean geometry of three dimensions. An even more abstract geometric notion of arbitrarily many dimensions is a metric space. It is based on only three axioms:

(1) The distance between two points is a positive number and is the same measured in either direction.

(2) The distance between any point and itself is zero.

(3) The sum of the lengths of two sides of a triangle is greater than the length of the third side.

Is it useful?

It is hard to see how a great deal of modern mathematics could be applied to other sciences and human affairs. Most of the men working on the frontiers of pure mathematics don't really care. They are interested primarily in creating ideas. Samuel Eilenberg of Columbia expresses this attitude when he compares himself facetiously with a tailor who makes coats for his own aesthetic satisfaction. "Sometimes I make them with five sleeves," he explains, "other times with seven sleeves. When it pleases me, I make a coat with two sleeves. And if it fits someone, I'm happy enough to have him wear it."

Eilenberg is confident, however, that his research, which is mainly in algebraic topology, will someday be applied by someone. Along with most pure mathematicians, he has an almost mystical faith in the utility of good mathematics—i.e., mathematics that is good by the aesthetic standards mathematicians apply to it. History supports this viewpoint. In

1858, for example, the English mathematician Arthur Cayley introduced the algebra of matrices—blocks of numbers arranged rectangularly in rows and columns. At the time Cayley said flatly that here was one form of mathematics no one would ever apply. Yet today theoretical physicists and engineers use matrices almost like a slide rule for computing many types of problems.

Another example is the non-Euclidean geometry that Bernhard Riemann invented in 1854. By assuming that lines cannot be parallel—i.e., they must meet at both ends, like meridians on the earth—he created a perfectly consistent geometry. Strange though it seemed at first, it became the mathematical language for describing the curved space of relativity. And when Einstein in developing relativity needed a mathematical tool to describe the fact that each observer has his own frame of reference in time-space, he reached back into mathematical history for tensor analysis, which had been invented some twenty years earlier by two Italians, Gregorio Ricci and Tullio T. Levi-Civita.

Still another instance of the applicability of pure mathematics is Hilbert space. When Hilbert first generalized Euclidean space to infinitely many dimensions, his notion seemed to have little relation to atomic physics. Yet today much of quantum mechanics is based on Hilbert space.

Reality

Einstein once observed: "As far as the laws of mathematics refer to reality, they are not certain; and

as far as they are certain, they do not refer to reality."
The present state of quantum mechanics bears him
out. There is, for example, a formula that describes
the interaction of a particle with a field of energy.
The first term of the formula is a close approximation
of what physicists actually observe. The second term
should refine the approximation. But it doesn't. The
second term and all that follow are, in fact, infinite.
Physicists combine the first approximation with the
finite parts of the rest of the formula, a trick that
mathematicians consider opportunistic, if not down-
right sloppy.

A group of young mathematicians, including
Professor Irving Segal of Chicago, is now trying to
repair the mathematical foundations of quantum
mechanics. Segal suspects that physicists are using
the wrong group concept. Newtonian mechanics is
based on the socalled Galilean group, which consists
of all the motions a rigid body can make. In this
group the distance between two nearby points does
not change. Relativistic mechanics, on the other hand,
depends on a more complicated group concept—the
Lorentz group, which combines time with the three
dimensions of ordinary space. (The relationship of
time to space is a very special one. The quantity that
remains unchanged is formulated mathematically as:
$dx^2 + dy^2 + dz^2 - dt^2$, where dx, dy, and dz are small
differences in length measured in the three dimensions of space and dt is a small difference in time.)
While the macroscopic world seems to fit the Lorentz
group, says Segal, the microcosm of subatomic particles may very well behave according to quite a dif-

ferent group of motions. He suspects that in addition to protons, electrons, neutrons, mesons, and the other particles physicists have discovered, there may be an infinite variety of fundamental particles—enough, in fact, to fill completely the range between the heaviest and the lightest. If this is true, and if the proper group concept could be found, physicists might be able to predict the nature of all the particles as successfully as they predicted the first meson.

Motivation

There are today many mathematicians who believe that their subject derives its richest inspirations from physical reality. They concentrate on mathematics that promises to have immediate practical applications.

Yet all mathematicians, pure or applied, are keenly aware that mathematics has a reality of its own. It is a reality that is defined in the human mind and need not be confirmed by the interpretation of a physical experiment. The physicist is fettered to whatever his instruments tell him is real; the mathematician, however, is free to explore a much richer world, mostly of his own making. In this freedom is the chief thrill of being a mathematician. Most research mathematicians today would agree with the nineteenth-century German mathematician, C. G. J. Jacobi, who, when asked why he did mathematics, replied: *"Pour l'honneur de l'esprit humain"*—to glorify the human intellect.

2

THE NEW USES OF THE ABSTRACT

Never before have so many people applied such abstract mathematics to so great a variety of problems. To meet the demands of industry, technology, and other sciences, mathematicians have had to invent new branches of mathematics and expand old ones. They have built a superstructure of fresh ideas that people trained in the classical branches of the subject would hardly recognize as mathematics at all.

Applied mathematicians have been grappling successfully with the world's problems at a time, curiously enough, when pure mathematicians seem almost to have lost touch with the real world. Mathematics has always been abstract, but pure mathematicians are pushing abstraction to new limits. To them mathematics is an art they pursue for art's sake, and they don't much care whether it will ever have any practical use.

Yet the very abstractness of mathematics makes it useful. By applying its concepts to worldly problems the mathematician can often brush away the

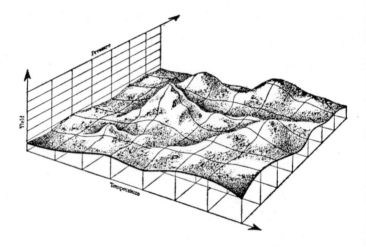

Geometry helps statisticians improve industrial products and processes, such as the hypothetical chemical process shown in the diagram above. Like a great many processes, it is hard to perfect because it responds in a very irregular way to changes in temperature and pressure. The statistician doesn't have to know any chemical theory to find out what temperature and pressure settings give the maximum yield —represented by the highest point on the "response surface." Rather, he approaches the problem like a blind man trying to find the highest peak in an unfamiliar country. The drawing at right illustrates his procedure. He starts with arbitrary settings and varies them slightly so that he can determine obscuring details and reveal simple patterns. Celestial mechanics, for example, enables astronomers to calculate the positions of the planets at any time in the past or future and to predict the comings and goings of comets. Now this ancient and abstruse branch of mathematics has suddenly become impressively practical for calculating orbits of earth satellites.

Even mathematical puzzles may have important applications. Mathematicians are still trying to find a

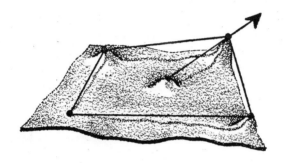

yields at the corners of a small square on the surface. If one corner is significantly higher than the others, he starts over again at that point and varies the settings to explore another small square. Successive steps lead him higher and higher. As the diagram at left makes evident, he could be misled by several topographic features—e.g., the small peak in the foreground, the ridge at the right, or the crest of the pass between the twin peaks in the rear. Such a response surface could just as well represent engine performance as fuel and carburetor adjustment vary, or any other measurable quantity. When there are many variables to consider, the geometry becomes more complicated, because the surface has as many dimensions as there are independent variables.

D

general rule for calculating the number of ways a particle can travel from one corner of a rectangular net to another corner without crossing its own path. When they solve this seemingly simple problem, they will be able to tell chemists something about the buildup of the long-chain molecules of polymers.

Mathematicians who are interested in down-to-earth problems have learned to solve many that were beyond the scope of mathematics only a decade or two ago. They have developed new statistical methods for controlling quality in high-speed industrial mass production. They have laid foundations for Operations Research techniques that businessmen use to schedule production and distribution. They have created an elaborate theory of "information" that enables communications engineers to evaluate precisely telephone, radio, and television circuits. They have grappled with the complexities of human behavior through game theory, which applies to military and business strategy alike. They have analyzed the design of automatic controls for such complicated systems as factory production lines and supersonic aircraft. Now they are ready to solve many problems of space travel, from guidance and navigation to flight dynamics of missiles beyond the earth's atmosphere.

Mathematicians have barely begun to turn their attention to the biological and social sciences, yet these once purely descriptive sciences are already taking on a new flavor of mathematical precision. Biologists are starting to apply information theory to inheritance. Sociologists are using sophisticated modern statistics to control their sampling. The bond between mathematics and the life sciences has been strengthened by the emergence of a whole group of applied mathematics specialties, such as biometrics, psychometrics, and econometrics.

Now that they have electronic computers, mathematicians are solving problems they would not have dared tackle a few years ago. In a matter of minutes they can get an answer that previously would have required months or even years of calculation. In designing computers and programing them to carry out instructions, furthermore, mathematicians have had to develop new techniques. While computers have as yet contributed little to pure mathematical theory, they have been used to test certain relationships among numbers. It now seems possible that a computer someday will discover and prove a brand-new mathematical theorem.

The unprecedented growth of U.S. mathematics, pure and applied, has caused an acute shortage of good mathematicians. Supplying this demand is a knotty problem. Mathematicians need more training than ever before; yet they can't afford to spend more years in school, for mathematicians are generally most creative when very young. A whole new concept of mathematical education, starting as early as the ninth grade, may offer the only escape from this dilemma.

Convenience of the outlandish

The applied mathematician must be a creative man. For applied mathematics is more than mere problem solving. Its primary goal is finding new mathematical approaches applicable to a wide range of problems. The same differential equation, for example, may describe the scattering of neutrons by atomic nuclei and the propagation of radio waves through the ionosphere. The same topological network may be a mathematical model of wires carrying current in an electric circuit and of gossips spreading rumors at a tea party. Because applied mathematics is inextricably tied to the problems it solves, the applied mathematician must be familiar with at least one other field—e.g., aerodynamics, electronics, or genetics.

The pure mathematician judges his work largely by aesthetic standards; the applied mathematician is a pragmatist. His job is to make abstract mathematical models of the real world, and if they work, he is satisfied. Often his abstractions are outlandishly farfetched. He may, for example, consider the sun as a mass concentrated at a point of zero volume, or he may treat it as a perfectly round and homogeneous sphere. Either model is acceptable if it leads to predictions that jibe with experiment and observation.

This matter-of-fact attitude helps to explain the radical changes in the long-established field of probability theory. Italian and French mathematicians broached the subject about three centuries ago to analyze betting odds for dice. Since then philosophers interested in mathematics have been seriously concerned about the nature of a mysterious "agency of chance." Working mathematicians, however, don't worry about the philosophic notion of chance. They consider probability as an abstract and undefined property—much as physicists consider mass or energy. In so doing, mathematicians have extended the techniques of probability theory to many problems that do not obviously involve the element of chance.

Probability today is almost like a branch of geometry. Each possible outcome of a particular experiment is treated as the location of a point on a line. And each repetition of the experiment is the coordinate of the point in another dimension. The probability of an outcome is a measure very much like the geometric measure of volume. Many problems in probability boil down to a geometric analysis of points scattered throughout a space of many dimensions.

One of the most fertile topics of modern probability theory is the so-called "random walk." A simple illustration is the gambler's ruin problem, in which two men play a game until one of them is bankrupt. If one starts with $100 and the other with $200 and they play for $1 a game, the progress of their gambling can be graphed as a point on a line 300 units (i.e., dollars) long. The point jumps one unit, right or left, each time the game is played, and when it reaches either end of the line, one gambler is broke. The problem is to calculate how long the game is likely to last and what chance each gambler has of winning.

Mathematicians have recently discovered some surprising facts about such games. When both players have unlimited capital and the game can go on indefinitely, the lead tends not to change hands nearly so often as most people would guess. In a game where both players have an equal chance of winning—such as matching pennies—after 20,000 plays it is about eighty-eight times as likely that the winner has led all the time as that the two players have shared the lead equally. No matter how long the game lasts, it is more likely that one player has led from the beginning than that the lead has changed hands any given number of times.

The random-walk abstraction is applicable to a great many physical situations. Some clearly involve chance—e.g., diffusion of gases, flow of automobile traffic, spread of rumors, progress of epidemic disease. The technique has even been applied to show that after the last glacial period seed-carrying birds must have helped re-establish the oak forests in the northern parts of the British Isles. But some modern random-walk problems have no obvious connection with chance. In a complicated electrical network, for example, if the voltages at the terminals are fixed, the voltages at various points inside the circuit can be calculated by treating the whole circuit as a sort of two-dimensional gambler's ruin game.

Risk versus gain

Mathematical statistics, the principal offshoot of probability theory, is changing just as radically as probability theory itself. Classical statistics has acted mainly as a tribunal, warning its users against drawing risky conclusions. The judgments it hands down are always somewhat equivocal, such as: "It is 98 per cent certain that drug A is at least twice as potent as drug B." But what if drug A is actually only half as potent? Classical statistics admits this possibility, but it does not evaluate the consequences. Modern statisticians have gone a step further with a new set of ideas known collectively as decision theory. "We now try to provide a guide to actions that must be taken under conditions of uncertainty," explains Herbert Robbins of Columbia. "The aim is to minimize the loss due to our ignorance of the true state of nature. In fact, from the viewpoint of game theory, statistical inference becomes the best strategy for playing the game called science."

The new approach is illustrated by the following example. A philanthropist offers to flip a coin once and let you call "heads" or "tails." If you guess right, he will pay you $100. You notice the coin is so badly bent and battered that it is much more likely to land on one side than the other. But you can't decide which side the coin favors. The philanthropist is willing to let you test the coin with trial flips, but he insists you pay him $1 for each experiment. How many trial flips should you buy before you make up your mind? The answer, of course, depends on how the trials turn out. If the coin lands heads up the first five times, you might conclude that it is almost certainly biased in favor of heads. But if you get three heads and two tails, you would certainly ask to experiment further.

Industry faces this kind of problem regularly. A manufacturer with a new product tests it before deciding whether to put it on the market. The more he tests, the surer he will be that his decision will be right. But tests cost money, and they take time. Now modern statistics can help him balance risk against gain and decide how long to continue testing. It can also help him design and carry out experiments. New methods involving a great deal of multidimensional geometry can point out how products and industrial processes can be improved. A statistician can often apply these methods to tune up a full-scale industrial plant without interrupting production. (For an example see the diagrams on pages 48 and 49.)

Classical statistics has been extended in another way. One of the latest developments is "non-parametric inference," a way of drawing conclusions about things that can be sorted according to size, longevity, dollar value, or any other graduated quality. What matters is the size of the statistical sample and the ranking of any particular object in that sample. It is not actually necessary to measure any of the objects, so long as they can be compared. It is possible to say, for instance, that if the sample consists of 473 objects, it is 99 per cent certain that only 1 per cent of all objects of this sort will be larger than the largest object in the sample. It makes no difference what the objects are—people, automobiles, ears of corn, or numbers drawn out of a hat. And the statement is still true if instead of largeness you consider smallness, intelligence, cruising speed, or any other relevant quality.

In practical application, non-parametric inference is being used to test batches of light bulbs. By burning a sample of sixty-three bulbs, for example, the manufacturer can conclude that 90 per cent of all the bulbs in the batch will almost certainly (99 chances out of 100) have a longer life than the second bulb to burn out during the test.

One of the most fascinating recent developments in applied mathematics is game theory, another off-shoot of probability theory. From a mathematical viewpoint, game theory is not particularly abstruse; many mathematicians, indeed, consider it shallow. But it is exciting because it has given mathematicians an analytic approach to human behavior.

Game theory is basically a mathematical description of competition among people or such groups of people as armies, corporations, or bridge partnerships. In theory, the players know all the possible outcomes of the competition and have a firm idea of what each outcome is worth to them. They are aware of all their possible strategies and those of their opponents. And invariably they behave "rationally" (though mathematicians are not sure just how to define "rational" behavior). Obviously, game theory represents a high degree of abstraction; people are never so purposeful and well informed, even in as circumscribed a competition as a game of chess. Yet the abstraction of man is valid to the extent that game theory is proving useful in analyzing business and military siuations.

When it was first developed in the Twenties, chiefly by Emile Borel in France and John von Neumann in Germany, game theory was limited to the simplest forms of competition. As late as 1944 the definitive book on the subject (*Theory of Games and*

Economic Behavior by von Neumann and Princeton economist Oskar Morgenstern) drew many of its illustrative examples from a form of one-card poker with limited betting between two people. Now, however, the strategies of two-person, zero-sum games (in which one player gains what his opponent loses) have been quite thoroughly analyzed. And game theorists have pushed on to more complex types of competition, which are generally more true to life.

Early game theory left much to be desired when it assumed that every plan should be designed for play against an all-wise opponent who would find out the strategy and adopt his own most effective counterstrategy. In military terms, this amounted to the assumption that the enemy's intelligence service was infallible. The game-theory solution was a randomly mixed strategy—one in which each move would be dictated by chance, say the roll of dice, so that the enemy could not possibly anticipate it. (For much the same reason the U.S. armed forces teach intelligence officers to estimate the enemy's capabilities rather than his intentions.) Many mathematicians have felt that this approach is unrealistically cautious. Recently game theorists have worked out strategies that will take advantage of a careless or inexpert opponent without risking anything if he happens to play shrewdly. (For a relatively simple example, see diagram on page 70.)

The most difficult games to analyze mathematically are those in which the players are not strictly competing with one another. An example is a labor-management negotiation; both sides lose unless they reach an agreement. Another complicating factor is collusion among players—e.g., an agreement between two buyers not to bid against each other. Still another is payment of money outside the framework of the "game," as when a large company holds a distributor in line by subsidizing him.

Who gets how much?

The biggest problem in analyzing such complex situations has been to find a mathematical procedure for distributing profits in such a way that "rational" players will be satisfied. One formula has been developed by Lloyd Shapley of the Rand Corporation. An outside arbitrator must decide the payments. The formula tells him how to give the players payments appropriate to the strength of their bargaining powers, and it also maximizes the total payment. There are obvious practical difficulties in applying Shapley's "arbitration value." In the first place, the payment, or value, each player receives can seldom be measured simply in dollars. Thus the arbitrator would have a hard time deciding on the proper distribution if the players were to lie about what they wanted to get from the game and how much they valued it.

While game theory has already contributed a great deal to decision theory in modern statistics, practical applications to complex human situations have not been strikingly successful. The chief troubles seem to be that there are no objective mathematical ways to formulate "rational" behavior or to measure the value of a given outcome to a particular player. At the very least, however, game theory has got mathematicians interested in analyzing human affairs and has stimulated more economists and social scientists to study higher mathematics. Game theory may be a forerunner of still more penetrating mathematical approaches that will someday help man to interpret more accurately what he observes about human behavior.

Universal tool

The backbone of mathematics, pure as well as applied, is a conglomeration of techniques known as "analysis." Analysis used to be virtually synonymous with the applications of differential and integral calculus. Modern analysts, however, use theorems and techniques from almost every other branch of mathematics, including topology, the theory of numbers, and abstract algebra.

In the last twenty or thirty years mathematical analysts have made rapid progress with differential equations, which serve as mathematical models for almost every physical phenomenon involving any sort of change. Today mathematicians know relatively simple routines for solving many types of differential equations on computers.

But there are still no straightforward methods for solving most non-linear differential equations—the kind that usually crop up when large or abrupt changes occur. Typical are the equations that describe the aerodynamic shock waves produced when an airplane accelerates through the speed of sound.

Russian mathematicians have concentrated enor-

HOW TO MAKE THE DIFFICULT SIMPLE

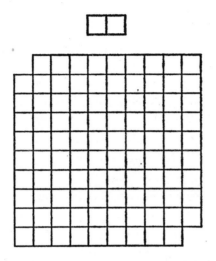

Problem: Given as many of the small rectangles as you want, can you arrange them to cover completely the large figure? None of the small rectangles must overlap or jut beyond the margins of the large figure. As it happens, the feat is impossible, but the difficult thing is to prove conclusively that it is impossible. For a mathematical solution, see page 62.

mous effort on the theory of non-linear differential equations. One consequence is that the Russians are now ahead of the rest of the world in the study of automatic control, and this may account for much of their success with missiles.

It is in the field of analysis that electronic computers have made perhaps their most important contri-

SOLUTION TO THE PROBLEM ON PAGE 61

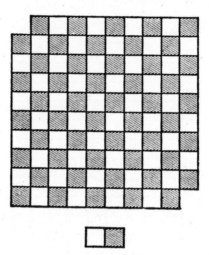

The key to the solution is to imagine that adjacent squares have different colors, as on a chessboard. Then it becomes obvious that each rectangle has to cover precisely one black square and one white square. Since the large figure contains unequal numbers of black and white squares, there can be no way to cover it with rectangles. The solution represents a conclusive negative proof, a logical feat that is peculiar to mathematics; in other sciences negative conclusions are invariably risky. The postulation of color is a relatively easy abstraction, but it is characteristic of some of the more complex abstractions that mathematicians use to simplify problems and theorems.

butions to applied mathematics. It still takes a skillful mathematician to set up a differential equation and interpret the solution. But in the final stages he can usually reduce the work to a numerical procedure— long and tedious, perhaps, but straightforward enough for a computer to carry out in a few minutes or at most a few hours. The very fact that computers are available makes it feasible to analyze mathematically a great many problems that used to be handled by various rules of thumb, and less accurately.

Mathematics of logic

Computers have also had some effects on pure mathematics. Faced with the problems of instructing computers what to do and how to do it, mathematicians have reopened an old and partly dormant field: Boolean algebra. This branch of mathematics reduces the rules of formal logic to algebraic form. Two of its axioms are startlingly different from the axioms of ordinary high-school algebra. In Boolean algebra $a+a=a$, and $a \times a=a$. The reason becomes clear when a is interpreted as a statement, the plus sign as "or," and the multiplication sign as "and." Thus, for example, the addition axiom can be illustrated by: "(this dress is red) or (this dress is red) means (this dress is red)."

Numerical analysis, a main part of the study of approximations, is another field that mathematicians have revived to program problems for computers. There is still a great deal of pure and fundamental mathematical research to be done on numerical errors that may arise through rounding off numbers. Computers are particularly liable to commit such errors, for there is a limit to the size of the numbers they can manipulate. If a machine gets a very long number, it has to drop the digits at the end and work with an approximation. While the approximation may be extremely close, the error may grow to be enormous if the number is multiplied by a large factor at a later stage of the problem. It is generally safe to assume that rounding off tends to even out in long arithmetic examples. In adding a long column of figures, for instance, you probably won't go far wrong if you consider 44.23 simply as 44, and 517.61 as 518. But it is sheer superstition to suppose that rounding off cannot possibly build up a serious accumulation of errors. (It obviously would if all the numbers happened to end in .499.)

There are subtler pitfalls in certain more elaborate kinds of computation. In some typical computer problems involving matrices that are used to solve simultaneous equations, John Todd of Caltech has constructed seemingly simple numerical problems that a computer simply cannot cope with. In some cases the computer gets grossly inaccurate results; in others it can't produce any answer at all. It is a challenge to numerical analysts to find ways to foresee this sort of trouble and then avoid it.

Patterns in primes

Computers have as yet made few direct contributions to pure mathematics except in the field of number theory. Here the results have been inconclusive but interesting. D. H. Lehmer of the University of California has had a computer draw up a list of all the prime numbers less than 46,000,000. (A prime is a number that is exactly divisible only by itself or one—e.g., 2, 3, 17, 61, 1,021.) A study of the list confirms that prime numbers, at least up to 46,000,000, are distributed among other whole numbers according to a "law" worked out theoretically about a century ago. The law states that the number of primes less than any given large number, X, is approximately equal to X divided by the natural logarithm of X. (Actually, the approximation is consistently a little on the low side.) Lehmer's list also tends to confirm conjectures about the distribution of twin primes—i.e., pairs of consecutive odd numbers both of which are primes, like 29 and 31, or 101 and 103. The number of twin primes less than X is roughly equal to X divided by the *square* of the natural logarithm of X.

Lehmer and H. S. Vandiver of the University of Texas have also used a computer to test a famous theorem that mathematicians the world over are still trying either to prove or disprove. Three hundred years ago the French mathematician Fermat stated that it is impossible to satisfy the following equation by substituting whole numbers (except zero) for all the letters if n is greater than 2:

$$a^n + b^n = c^n$$

Lehmer and Vandiver have sought to find a single exception. If they could, the theorem would be disproved. Fortunately they have not had to test

E

every conceivable combination of numbers; it is sufficient to try substituting all prime numbers for n. And there are further short cuts. The number n for example must not divide any of a certain set of so-called "Bernoulli numbers," otherwise it cannot satisfy the equation. (The Bernoulli numbers are irregular. The first is $1/6$; the third, $1/30$; the eleventh, $691/2,730$; the thirteenth, $7/6$; the seventeenth, $43,867/798$; the nineteenth, $1,222,277/2,310$. Numbers later in the series are enormous.)

Lehmer and Vandiver have tested the Fermat theorem for all prime n's up to 4,000, but they seem to be coming to a dead end. The Bernoulli numbers at this stage are nearly 10,000 digits long, and even a fast computer takes a full hour to test each n. The fact that a machine has failed to find an exception does not, of course, prove the Fermat theorem, although it does perhaps add a measure of assurance that the theorem is true.

But it is possible for a computer to produce a mathematical proof. Allen Newell of Rand Corporation and Herbert A. Simon of Carnegie Tech have worked out a program of instructions that tells a high-speed computer how to work out proofs of some elementary theorems in mathematical logic contained in *Principia Mathematica*, a three-volume treatise by Alfred North Whitehead and Bertrand Russell.

The Newell and Simon program is based on heuristic thinking—the kind of hunch-and-analogy approach that a creative human mind uses to simplify complicated problems. The computer is supplied with some basic axioms, and it stores away all theorems it has previously proved. When it is told to prove an unfamiliar theorem, it first tries to draw analogies and comparisons with the theorems it already knows. In many cases the computer produces a logical proof within a few minutes; in others it fails to produce any proof at all. It would conceivably be possible to program a computer to solve theorems with an algorithmic approach, a sure-fire, methodical procedure for exhausting all possibilities. But such a program might take years for the fastest computer to carry out.

Although most mathematicians scoff at the idea, Newell and Simon are confident that heuristic programing will soon enable computers to do truly creative mathematical work. They guess that within ten years a computer will discover and prove an important mathematical theorem that never occurred to any human mathematician.

Help wanted

But computers are not going to put mathematicians out of work. Quite to the contrary, computers have opened up so many new applications for mathematics that industrial job opportunities for mathematicians have more than doubled in the last five years. About one-fourth of the 250 people who are getting Ph.D.'s in mathematics this year are going into industry—chiefly aircraft, electronics, communications, and petroleum companies. In 1946 only about one in nine Ph.D.'s took jobs in industry.

While most companies prefer mathematicians

who have also had considerable background in physics or engineering, many companies are also eager to hire men who have concentrated on pure mathematics. Starting pay for a good young mathematician with a fresh Ph.D. now averages close to $10,000 a year in the aircraft industry, about double that of 1950 (and about double today's starting pay in universities).

Still, a great deal of industrial mathematics is done by physicists and engineers who have switched to mathematics after graduation. And there is also room for people with bachelor's and master's degrees, particularly in programing computers to perform calculations.

Different companies use mathematicians in different ways. Some incorporate them in research teams along with engineers, physicists, metallurgists, and other scientists. But a growing number have set up special mathematics groups, which carry out their own research projects and also do a strictly limited amount of problem solving for other scientific departments.

The oldest and most illustrious industrial mathematics department was set up in 1930 by Bell Telephone Laboratories. It started with only six or eight professional mathematicians and grew slowly until after the war. Then in ten years it doubled in size. Today the department has about thirty professional mathematicians, half of them with Ph.D.'s in mathematics, the rest with Ph.D.'s in other sciences. The department has made outstanding contributions to mathematics. Notable is information theory, which was developed during and after the war by Claude Shannon as a mathematical model for language and its communication.

Crisis in education

The demand for mathematicians of every sort is rapidly outstripping the capacity of the U.S. educational system. Swelling enrollments in mathematics courses are already beginning to tax college and university mathematics departments. At Princeton, for example, the mathematics majors have for years numbered only five to ten, but nineteen members of 1957's junior class elected to major in mathematics. To complicate matters further, the good college and university departments no longer require their professors to teach twelve to fifteen hours a week. So that the teachers can also do research, the average classroom time has been reduced to nine hours in most schools, and to less than six in some of the best universities. Yet the serious mathematics student now needs more training than ever before. If he wants a good job in industry or in a top university he must have a doctor's degree; and if he wants to excel in research he should have a year or two of postdoctoral study.*

* The schools most highly rated by mathematicians are: Chicago, Harvard, and Princeton. Next come Brown, California, Columbia, Cornell, Johns Hopkins, Illinois, Indiana, M.I.T., Michigan, Stanford, Virginia, and Yale. A special case is New York University's Institute of Mathematical Sciences, which with government financing has become the national capital of applied mathematical analysis. Another special case is the Institute for Advanced Study at Princeton, a haven for postdoctoral students who want to continue their education and do research.

HOW TO PLAY SMARTER THAN SAFE

Early workers in game theory designed strategies that were safe to use against infallible opponents, but mathematicians now know ways to take advantage of a careless opponent without risking anything. The diagram dictates the best strategy for guessing whether your opponent has placed a concealed coin heads up or tails up. If he were wise, he would mix heads and tails randomly, simply by flipping the coin each time. In that case, you could do no better than break even in the long run. But if he tries to anticipate your guesses, the strategy in the diagram enables you to win whenever he follows any regular pattern; and in any event you will do no worse than break even in the long run.

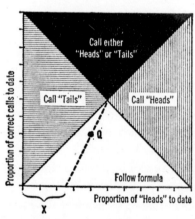

As the game progresses, you keep track of the proportion of times your opponent has placed the coin heads up and the proportion of times you have won. This determines the point Q. When Q is in the black or gray triangles, you follow the pure strategies shown in the diagram. But when Q is in the white triangle, you must adopt a mixed strategy, which you calculate as follows: Draw a line connecting the center of the diagram with Q and extending to the base line. The length x determines your strategy. Since x is in this case ¾, you should adopt some random way of calling heads or tails that makes it three times as likely that you will call tails. (You might put four slips of paper in a hat—three of them marked tails—and draw one.) This method takes advantage of your opponent's apparent tendency to place the coin tails up, yet it keeps him from guessing your strategy. If you follow this plan, the point Q should ultimately end up in the black triangle, which represents a profit for you.

There is a great deal to be mastered in modern mathematics, but surprisingly it is relatively easier to learn than most of the mathematics traditionally taught in high school and college, despite its abstractness and complexity. One change that would obviously help would be to start teaching the important modern concepts and techniques earlier. The way mathematics is taught now, complains John G. Kemeny of Dartmouth, "it is the only subject you can study for fourteen years [i.e., through sophomore calculus] without learning anything that's been done since the year 1800."

The Dartmouth plan

Some colleges are now making progress in modernizing their mathematics curricula. Several no longer require a special course in trigonometry. "We really don't have to train everybody to be a surveyor," explains one department head. Under the leadership of Kemeny, Dartmouth in the last five years has almost completely revised its undergraduate course. There are now, in fact, three separate courses of study in mathematics: one for mathematics majors, another for engineers and others who must have mathematical training, and a third for the liberal-arts students who want to make mathematics part of their cultural background.

The courses are amazingly popular. Ninety per cent of all Dartmouth students take at least one semester of mathematics, and more than 60 per cent finish a year of it (mathematics is an elective for most of them). Kemeny and two associates have written for one of their courses a remarkable textbook entitled *Introduction to Finite Mathematics*. Within a year after its publication in January, 1957, it was being used by about 100 colleges, in some cases just for mathematics courses especially designed for social-science majors. And several New York high schools have adopted the book for special sections of exceptional students.

Mathematics for children

The movement to teach more mathematics and teach it sooner has filtered down to the secondary-school level. The College Entrance Examination Board, through its commission on mathematics, has drawn up a program for modernizing secondary-school mathematics courses. The chief aim of the commission, according to its executive director, Albert E. Meder, is to give students an appreciation of the true meaning of mathematics and some idea of modern developments. Algebra, he points out, is no longer a "disconnected mass of memorized tricks but a study of mathematical structure; geometry no longer a body of theorems arranged in a precise order that can be memorized without understanding."

The College Board has the support of most leading mathematicians. About twenty of them met with twenty high-school mathematics teachers in the summer of 1958 at Yale to write outlines of sample textbooks based partly on the College Board's recommendations. This group, headed by E. G. Begle of Yale, plans to write the actual books within the next year so that teachers and commercial publishers will know how mathematicians think mathematics ought to be taught in high school.

Perhaps the most radical step in U.S. mathematical education has been taken by the University of Illinois' experimental high school. There, under the guidance of a member of the university's mathematics department, a professor of education, Max Beberman, has introduced a completely new mathematics curriculum. It starts with an informal axiomatic approach to arithmetic and algebra and proceeds through aspects of probability theory, set theory, number theory, complex numbers, mathematical induction, and analytic geometry. The approach reflects the rigor, abstractness, and generality of modern mathematics. To make room for some of the new concepts, Beberman and his advisers have had to reduce the amount of time spent drilling on such techniques as factoring algebraic expressions.

So far the experiment has been very stimulating to students—partly, of course, because of the very fact that the course is an experiment. In the college entrance examinations of 1957, the first group of students to complete four years of the Illinois course made some of the highest scores in the nation.

While twelve other high schools have now experimentally adopted the Illinois mathematics curriculum, it is not likely to be widely used for some time. The reason is that most high-school teachers have to be completely retrained to teach it. With Carnegie Foundation support, the University of Illinois has begun to train high-school teachers from many states to teach the new curriculum.

For many years it has been hard for a would-be teacher to learn what mathematics he needs to teach any serious high-school course. Professor George Pólya of Stanford explains: "The mathematics department [of a university] offers them tough steak they cannot chew, and the school of education vapid soup with no meat in it." The National Science Foundation has helped more than fifty colleges and universities set up institutes where high-school teachers can study mathematics for a summer or even a full academic year.

Opportunity ahead

However many mathematicians there may be, there will always be a need for more first-rate minds to create new mathematics. This will be true of applied mathematics as well as pure mathematics. For applied mathematics now presents enough of an intellectual challenge to attract even academic men who pride themselves on creating mathematics for its own sake. One young assistant professor, recently offered $16,000 by industry, is seriously thinking of abandoning his university career. He explains: "I think that the problems in applied mathematics would offer me just as much stimulation as more basic research."

Whole new fields of mathematics are needed to cope with problems in other sciences and human affairs. Transportation engineers, for example, still lack a mathematical method to analyze the turbulence of four-lane highway traffic; and it may be years before they can apply precise mathematical reasoning to three-dimensional air traffic. Biologists have used almost no mathematics aside from statistics, but now some of them are seriously thinking of applying topology. This branch of mathematics, which deals with generalized shapes and disregards size, may be the most appropriate way to describe living cells with their enormous variations in size and shape. Neurophysiologists are looking for a new kind of algebra to represent thinking processes, which are by no means random, yet not entirely methodical.

There are still some remarkably simple questions that are teasing mathematicians. They have not yet found, for example, a general solution to the following problem: Given a road map of N folds, how many ways can you refold it? And when this is solved, there will be another puzzle, and another.

3

THE NEXT GENERATION OF COMPUTERS

The new computers will be twenty to a hundred times faster than today's million-dollar machines. Their layouts are so elaborate that a computer is needed to design them. Their timing will be so exquisite that electronic pulses surging through wires at nearly the speed of light may be occasionally too sluggish for them. And they will be expensive. The first of the new machines, due to be completed this year and next, will cost about $3 million apiece, almost twice as much as the biggest computers now in existence. But at that price their immense capacity for work makes them truly bargains, and their complexity paradoxically makes them comparatively easy to operate.

There are innovations aplenty in the new machines—e.g., faster-acting circuits that employ transistors and more novel components. But the major difference between the new generation of computers and their predecessors is the principle of parallel operation. The parallel computers, as the designers call them, are really two or three big computers harnessed together and working as a battery.

Happily, the designers are making it possible for the new machines to program their own operations in large measure, for a human operator would be overwhelmed by the job of keeping track of the interplay of the various units in order to schedule the work step by step. With several operations going on simultaneously, the program will have to determine not only what the computer is to do but precisely when it must do it. The machines will direct their own traffic of information. All the human programer can be expected to do is indicate roughly the logical sequence of operations.

With automatic programing, moreover, the computers can act on relatively simple instructions. A man with a problem to solve will be able to order the computer to get at it in a language much like ordinary English, and he will get back his answer without having to know what went on inside the machine in the meantime.

The new computers are arriving at an opportune time. There are now in the U.S. some 400 computers in the million-dollar-and-up class, and the number has been doubling roughly every year. But there is a ceiling on the demand for today's big computers, because the solutions to many of the problems that scientists, engineers, and businessmen want to put to the machines take too long and therefore cost too much at present-day computer speeds.

The parallel computers will eventually translate languages, notably technical Russian, faster and cheaper than a human can. For nuclear physicists they will determine with precision the behavior of particles. They will help military and business men reach more logical decisions.

But even before the first of the new computers has been completed, research scientists are looking far ahead, to other generations of machines that will imitate human thought processes—computers that will employ judgment and a kind of intuition to solve problems. Someday, conceivably, probably more than a century from now, scientists will build a machine much faster and more compact than the human brain —and almost as versatile.

The automatic traffic cop

Heretofore, computers have been able to handle only one operation at a time. Some parts of the machines have inevitably been idle at any given time. Arithmetic units, for example, have had to pause for as long as several seconds while input units searched for data in reels of magnetic tape. It has never been practical to store all the data in magnetic cores and other fast-acting memory components, from which information can be retrieved in about a millionth of a second, because the components are too expensive: they cost about $1 per "bit" of information.

In the new computers waiting time will be cut to a minimum. The scheme of the National Bureau of Standards' Pilot is typical. A primary computer will do most of the arithmetical calculations. A smaller secondary computer will act as traffic cop, keeping track of various parts of the program, and occasionally helping calculate parts of the problem. Meanwhile, a third computer will control incoming and outgoing data. It will anticipate what information the primary computer will need, search for it through several reels of magnetic tape simultaneously, convert the data to usable form, and pass it on to the primary computer at just the right instant. Internal traffic jams will be solved in a small fraction of a second.

Pilot is to be finished this summer. Next year Remington Rand, a division of Sperry Rand Corp., will probably install Larc (for Livermore Advanced Research Computer) at the University of California's Livermore radiation laboratory. Both machines will be roughly twenty times as fast as the I.B.M. 709, one of the best of today's scientific computers. Stretch, an I.B.M. computer destined for the Los Alamos Scientific Laboratory, will be even faster when it is completed in 1960.

Most designers feel that in the new computers they will have pushed the speed of components close to a practical limit. Coded information will race through the machines at the rate of two million or more pulses per second, each one timed to within a few hundred-millionths of a second. Pulses move at a rate of almost a billion feet per second, but a twenty-

ROULETTE BY COMPUTER:
The Monte Carlo method and a problem in physics

To mathematicians "the Monte Carlo method" is not a way of breaking the bank but a way of determining probabilities in a complex situation by playing a game of chance. The point is to play the game thousands of times—and so a computer is essential. The hypothetical example shown here shows how a nuclear physicist would use the Monte Carlo method to calculate the effectiveness of a new shielding material—i.e., what proportion of subatomic particles it would screen out, absorb, or allow to pass through.

The rules of the "game" are stated in the table at right. The black and white dots in the diagram represent the arrangement of two kinds of atoms in the shield. The computer determines each move by generating a "random number." (Without a computer you could do the same by spinning a roulette wheel or throwing dice.) The particle that followed path 2, for example, made its moves according to the following sequence of numbers: 3, 18, 33, 4, 26, 20, 19, 22, 34, 25, 5, 32, 36, 36, 31, 24, 34, 26, 35, 36, 35. It was finally thrust out from the bottom of the shield. It is assumed that the shield stretches indefinitely to the left and right; path 4, after leaving the right edge of the array of dots, re-entered in a corresponding position on the left edge. The behavior of particles in this example is unrealistically simple, yet sufficiently complex so that a physicist would find it hard to calculate by probability theory how well the shield would work.

This particular problem was actually worked out on an I.B.M. 704. The program of instructions, written in Fortran automatic coding, told the machine to generate a rectangular mesh of 72 white atoms and 648 black atoms in a random arrangement; generate a random number to determine where a particle entered the mesh; generate more random numbers

Particle's next move...	...if it starts on black and the number is:	...if it starts on white and the number is:
Absorbed	1	1, 2, or 3
Three forward	2 or 3	———
Two forward	4, 5, or 6	4
One forward	7, 8, 9, or 10	5, 6, or 7
One right, one forward	11, 12, 13, 14, or 15	8, 9, 10, or 11
One left, one forward	16, 17, 18, 19, or 20	12, 13, 14, or 15
One right	21, 22, or 23	16, 17, 18, or 19
One left	24, 25, or 26	20, 21, 22, or 23
One right, one backward	27, 28, 29, or 30	24, 25, 26, 27, or 28
One left, one backward	31, 32, 33, or 34	29, 30, 31, 32, or 33
One backward	35 or 36	34 or 35
Two backward	———	36

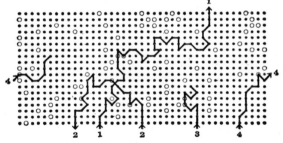

to determine each subsequent move; make the moves; note when a particle was absorbed, was reflected, or passed through the far side; and print the results. In just seven and a half minutes the computer simulated 7,600 particles, making a total of 91,476 moves—an average of six seconds per hundred particles. More than half of the time was spent printing results. The shield absorbed 39.2 per cent of the particles, reflected 45.4 per cent, and passed 15.4 per cent.

foot-long wire would slow them down enough to im-
peril the accuracy of the computer's timing.

Faced with such problems, it is hardly surprising
that designers have had to use existing computers to
help them plan the parallel computers. Remington
Rand used a Univac I to calculate an efficient wiring
diagram for Larc. The Univac spent fifty hours typing
out a list of some 60,000 connections; it even specified
which wires should be shielded. Alan L. Leiner, chief
architect of Pilot, worked out his wiring on an I.B.M.
704. He now plans to make the 704 in its own relatively slow fashion mimic the operation of the Pilot
and draw up a special program for maintenance men.
When something goes wrong with Pilot, the program
will write a diagnosis of the trouble in a form of symbolic logic.

Waiting to be computed

There is already a long list of problems waiting
for the new computers. They will be able to solve
most of these with standard mathematical methods,
although mathematicians will in the next few years
very likely develop new methods to exploit the speed
of the new machines.

It is no coincidence that two of the first new computers are going to atomic-energy laboratories, for
nuclear physicists are eager to work on "many-body"
problems concerning the interaction of particles and
their electromagnetic forces. In many instances the
bodies are too few to allow the problem to be solved
by the statistical methods of quantum mechanics or

thermodynamics; at the same time they are so numerous that today's biggest computers would take weeks or months to perform the calculations.

Some other kinds of problems that mathematicians have been solving by techniques developed especially for computers have outgrown the speed and capacity of present-day machines. A typical example is linear programing, which some companies use to plan product distribution, manufacturing schedules, and other complex business operations. A linear program consists of a great many statements concerning the interrelationships of various factors that have to be considered in reaching a decision. A sample statement: "Selling price is greater than manufacturing cost plus sales commission." These statements are all expressed symbolically as a rectangular array of numbers called a "matrix." By manipulating the matrix, a mathematician can arrive at optimal plans—e.g., a plan that maximizes profit, or one that minimizes time. In their exploration of linear programing, mathematicians have encountered many real-life situations —such as the operation of an oil refinery—that require matrices as big as 200 rows by 1,000 columns. Manipulating such an enormous matrix requires 2x200x200x1,000, or 80 million, separate multiplications—a job worthy of the new computers.

Mathematicians are also having trouble fitting some Monte Carlo calculations into today's computers. The Monte Carlo method is a way of representing a complex phenomenon—a battle, say, or a pattern of atomic radiation—as a game of chance.

The "game" is played over and over by computer, perhaps hundreds of thousands of times. The outcome gives a good indication of what would happen in the real situation. (For a hypothetical application of Monte Carlo to nuclear physics, see pages 80 and 81.) The new computers will greatly expand the scope of Monte Carlo. With computing speed to spare, mathematicians will be able to afford to make the rules of the game far more complex so as to reflect real situations with much greater accuracy.

Simulation is another field that needs the speed of the new computers. For several years the armed services have been working out logistics support, strategic air maneuvers, and other dynamic systems on computers. It is possible, for example, to see how the Air Material Command would function under all-out enemy attack. With high-speed computers, several weeks of action are compressed into an experiment that takes only a few days. The new computers will carry out such experiments still faster, in greater detail, and more cheaply.

Talking to an idiot child

The new computers would have been impossible without the invention of automatic programing, which has immeasurably increased the usefulness of present-day machines.

It has been said that a computer must be instructed as painstakingly as if one were addressing an idiot child. Only the simplest "knowledge" is built into a computer. It can identify its own "memory" locations, the banks of magnetic cores or sections of tape in which names and numbers are stored. But it does not know what is in any given memory location. It can do elementary arithmetic. And it can perform a few logical operations, such as comparing the size of two numbers. But when a programer wants to make a machine multiply two numbers, for example, he must furnish the plan. He must write out in code the memory locations of each number, an instruction to multiply, and the memory location in which the result is to be stored.

In planning and coding operations for a computer, even the best programers may make mistakes. The average programer makes a great many, for programing exacts the utmost in precise and orderly thinking. For instance, a programer may misremember the memory location he assigned to a particular number. By the time he has written out the program for solving the problem, checked back and corrected his errors, the operation is likely to cost about $5 per instruction. Most programs contain hundreds of instructions, and many contain thousands.

Short cuts in codes

To be sure, programers have developed short cuts in their work. Almost every problem presented to them involves some operations that have been coded before in connnection with an earlier problem. If a programer wants the computer, say, to take the square root of a number, he has a stock of coded square-root-taking routines. Programers constantly use mathematical routines already worked out by others, and several organizations have been set up to pool programs and sections of programs. It still takes ingenuity to fit the precoded pieces together, but program pools have to date saved computer users probably well over $100 million.

Programers for the parallel computers will probably never have to write machine code. Instead, they will use "compilers." First suggested by Grace Murray Hopper, who heads Remington Rand's automatic programing development, compilers are magnetic tapes on which are coded most of the common mathematical routines plus a master tape that instructs the computer how to put together various combinations of the routines. At present each make and model of computer needs its own compiler, but universal compilers that will work on any big computer are certain to be developed.

To the operator of a computer, a compiler provides a special language for writing out orders to the machine. Almost anyone can read the language after a little practice, for it is based on ordinary English and mathematical notation. In Remington Rand's Math-Matic compiler, for example, the operator writes "sine A" as "SIN A" on a typewriter that simultaneously prints the letters on paper and puts coded spots on magnetic tape. "Nth root of A" becomes "N ROOT A" and "Cube root of A" becomes "$A^{\frac{1}{3}}$." I.B.M.'s equivalent compiler, known as Fortran (for "formula translation"), employs similar terminology. (In the future, however, compilers for mathematics will probably use an artificial international language now being developed for the purpose by U.S. and European computer experts.)

Compilers for business data have been more difficult to make up than compilers for mathematical work. Unlike mathematics, business has few standard notations; terminology and methods of keeping files vary from company to company. Also, business procedures are changed frequently and sometimes radically. After working out a new contract with a union, for example, a company may have to make major changes in its program for payroll computation. And a program for a big company is apt to be enormous: U.S. Steel's payroll computation alone takes 90,000 coded instructions.

Remington Rand has a data-processing compiler called Flow-Matic, a special language for payroll computation, inventory control, and other business operations. Flow-Matic is easily read by laymen. Typical instruction in computing a payroll: MULTIPLY HRS-WORKED (B) BY RATE (A) GIVING GROSS-PAY (A). Another: SUBTRACT UNION-DUES (A) AND BOND-DEDUCT (A) FROM ADJUST-PAY (A); STORE THE REMAINDER IN ADJUST-PAY (A). The letters in parentheses refer to the magnetic-tape files where the data is to be found or stored.

Some experienced programers complain that automatic programing produces inefficient machine codes because it is inflexible. But by and large, computer users have found that automatic programing pays off. What they save in programing time more than makes up for what they may lose in computing time. Furthermore, in actual tests compilers have "written" better programs than the average professional programer turns out.

Automatic programing pays off in other ways. Professional programers are hard to find and expensive to train. But now, instead of spending about ten weeks learning machine code, a programer needs only two or three days to master a compiler language. The time will come when clerical workers with a little special training will probably do most of the programing for day-to-day computer problems.

Even people who do not intend to be programers will find it desirable to learn automatic programing. A growing number of business executives and laboratory directors are in fact doing so now. By programing a computer themselves they develop a feel for the kinds of problems a machine can solve and how long it takes to solve them.

Thinking by electronics

Computer designers have taken a giant step forward with the parallel computers, but they are not yet in sight of the ultimate goal: a thinking machine. The scientists and mathematicians who are working toward electronic systems that will do creative thinking may have to develop an entirely new technology. Meanwhile researchers are devising special problem-solving programs that can be run off on present-day computers. Herbert L. Gelernter and Nathaniel Rochester of I.B.M. have worked out a program that uses ingenuity to solve problems in plane geometry. Arthur Samuel of I.B.M. has made a computer play checkers expertly. Other mathematicians have reduced symbolic differentiation (a process of calculus) to formulas a computer can apply.

Some of the most enlightening research has been done on chess-playing programs. Chess is a particularly good way to study thought processes because, as M.I.T. mathematician Claude Shannon explains, "chess is a compact little universe. It is a simplified and abstracted form of what we face in the physical world. It has conflict, logic, goals, and rules. And if we can puzzle these out, we will have clues for the more important and complex things."

For all practical purposes, chess is impossible to analyze exhaustively. On most plays a player has a choice of twenty or thirty moves; not even the fastest computer could study all the possibilities that might follow one move. Human players simplify the problem by eliminating most of the possible moves and concentrating on those that their judgment tells them are promising. It is this kind of judgment that researchers want to build into computer programs.

Alex Bernstein of I.B.M., a former intercollegiate chess champion, has written a chess program that has actually played a full game. It can beat a beginner, but loses to any passable amateur because the computer looks ahead only four moves (two by each player). The machine considers all the possible moves and evaluates them according to a formula which takes into account the advantages of castling, capturing a piece, etc. Then it selects the seven most "valuable" moves and analyzes each one four plays ahead. Thus, to make a move, the machine has to evaluate only 7x7x7x7 positions. Even so, it takes an average of eight minutes to make a move.

A more elaborate—and even more cumbersome —chess-playing program is being developed by Allen Newell and J. C. Shaw of Rand Corp. with Herbert Simon of Carnegie Tech. Their aim is to make the computer evaluate various goals—e.g., the capture of enemy pieces as against control of the center squares of the board. Under this program it is estimated that the machine will spend from one to ten hours on each move.

Other research scientists are working on the more practical, and more challenging, problem of translating languages with computers. A human translator, of course, has to know a good deal more than the words that correspond to each other in the languages he handles. He has to recognize idioms and colloquialisms. He has to know grammar. He has to pick the correct meaning for words that are spelled alike but have different meanings. And he often has to differentiate among various shades of meanings.

A program that will direct a computer to perform all these operations in translating Russian into English is the goal of a group of Rand scientists. Their hope is that the computer will produce an English text nearly as clear and readable as an expert translator's. To this end, the scientists are studying 250,000 words of Russian text, recording the meaning of each word in context and in relation to other words in the text. The program will, in effect, be a Russian glossary plus a grammar more detailed than any ever prepared anywhere, even in Russia.

Another group working on German with a similar approach is headed by physicist Victor H. Yngve and linguist William N. Locke of M.I.T. Yngve hopes to produce smooth translations at a cost of ¾ cent per word (as against the average of 2 cents for human translators). "I've learned a great deal about teaching German," says Locke. "We now have a formula for German word order that our beginning students can understand. And we can tell them how to make a compound noun; the rules are not in any grammar book, yet they do exist. Who knows how many details like this grammarians have missed?"

Good, gooder, goodest

Since 1950 the U.S. Government has spent more than $1 million on research in this field. The first breakthrough, oddly enough, will probably come from a one-woman project. The woman is Mrs. Ida Rhodes, a Russian-born mathematician and computer programer at the National Bureau of Standards. Her program instructs the machine, first, to change the words of a Russian sentence into a greatly condensed form of a special glossary she has evolved; second, to recognize the syntactical relation between words; and finally, to put together their English correspondents into a meaningful sentence.

To conserve precious memory space, Mrs. Rhodes

How a computer found lucky numbers

Stanislaw Ulam of the Los Alamos Scientific Laboratory, who with the late John von Neumann was among the first top-flight mathematicians to take an interest in computers, recently created a new sequence of numbers, which he calls "lucky numbers." He programed a computer to do the following:

(1) List all the whole numbers from 1 to 48,600.
(2) Consider the first number, aside from 1, and call it N. Then strike out every Nth number.
(3) Among the remaining numbers, consider the first, aside from 1 and N, and call it M. Then strike out every Mth number.
(4) Repeat the process until it fails to strike out any more numbers.

After the first stage, the computer had left only the odd numbers: 1,3,5,7,9,11, etc. After the second stage, the sequence started: 1,3,7,9,13,15,19. The final list, consisting of 4,571 lucky numbers, began: 1,3,7,9,13,15,21,25,31.

Ulam discovered some facts about lucky numbers that have fascinated mathematicians interested in the extremely abstract branch of mathematics known as number theory. Lucky numbers are strikingly similar to primes—i.e., numbers that leave a remainder when divided by any other number. Between 1 and 48,600 there are 5,000 primes, 4,571 luckies. Of these, 715 are both prime and lucky. Corresponding to Goldbach's conjecture, a famous unproved theorem about primes, every even number seems to be the sum of two lucky numbers.

plans to bypass for the present instructions dealing with the refinements of English grammar. She prefers to concentrate her efforts on having the final translation convey faithfully the import of the original text. So she treats all words as if they were regular. Thus the comparative of "good" will be "good-er." The past tense of "go" will be "go-ed." And the plural of "mouse" will be "mouse-s."

The infant thinker

While most of the advanced programing research is highly specialized, a few mathematicians are taking a general approach to problem-solving. Newell, Shaw and Simon at Rand and Carnegie Tech are building a high-level program that will supervise the solving of a variety of problems. They are building into it the logical steps common to solving problems in abstract logic, trigonometry, and several other fields.

John McCarthy of M.I.T. is aiming still higher: he is devising a system of feeding a computer declarative sentences from which it can create its own program. At a recent Symposium on the Mechanization of Thought Processes held in Teddington, England, he described how his program could, in theory, decide that a man should drive to a nearby airport. He would give the machine a list of facts: "I am at my desk. My desk is at home. My car is at home. My home is in the county. The airport is in the county. I can walk anywhere in my home. I can drive my car anywhere in the county." He would also supply logical rules for deduction. Then he would ask the computer: "If I want to reach the airport, what do I do?" The problem is infantile, to be sure, but the computer would have to do some thinking on its own.

Stanislaw Ulam, of the Los Alamos Scientific Laboratory, is urging researchers to study still another approach to mechanized thinking. His idea is to make man and machine cooperate, with the man supplying the intuitive ideas and the machine doing the onerous calculations. Ulam believes that theoretical mathematicians and physicists would find computers invaluable if they followed his scheme. With a few attachments a super-computer could be converted to a super-scratch pad. A mathematician might, for example, use such a machine to perform intellectual experiments. He would have the computer display on a cathode-ray screen various cross-sections of geometric figures, which he could examine from any angle. While the computer would not in any sense be doing creative thinking, it could give an intuitive human mind examples to ponder.

Research on mechanized thought is inevitably converging with research on the human brain. The difficulties involved in building a machine that acts like a brain at this point seem insurmountable.

In the first place, as John von Neumann pointed out shortly before his death, scientists are still unaware of the "programing" code that must exist within the brain. He explained: "Logic and mathematics in the central nervous system, when viewed as languages, must be structurally essentially different from those languages to which our common experience refers." Then, too, the organization of the brain's neurons (nerve cells) is utterly unknown. Many connections or circuits among neurons in the brain seem to be entirely arbitrary. If a part of the brain is damaged, it can to a large extent reorganize its circuits and continue to function reliably.

Some scientists are now trying to design machines that in some respects respond like rudimentary brains. Frank Rosenblatt, a young psychologist at the Cornell Aeronautical Laboratory, is building an electronic network that will recognize shapes. He calls it the Perceptron. It is to consist of a bank of photocells and 1,000 variable potentiometers interconnected arbitrarily. When the photocells perceive something—say, the letter A—they will produce a voltage which will adjust some of the potentiometers. There will be a reinforcing mechanism: every time the Perceptron "sees" an A, the output will nudge a feedback circuit that makes the response to A increasingly stronger. Eventually, Rosenblatt predicts, the Perceptron will recognize A even if the letter is sloppily written, partially erased, or strangely slanted.

Other scientists are seeking to duplicate the brain's mechanism in hardware. A few years ago they despaired of making an electronic machine as compact as the brain, for each of the ten billion neurons in the brain is equivalent roughly to an electronic switch. Someday soon, however, they will have components as small as neurons and probably a great deal more reliable. Dudley Buck at M.I.T. is developing a microscopic switch called a cryotron that operates at extremely low temperature, and Kenneth Shoulders of Stanford Research Institute is perfecting another kind of electronic switch one-thousandth as thick as the point of a phonograph needle. Meanwhile, neuro-physiologist Jerome Lettvin of M.I.T. has invented a simple transistor network that behaves like a single neuron. By replacing transistors with Buck's or Shoulders' tiny switches, he hopes to make an electronic neuron that is actually smaller than a human neuron.

The problem of organizing electronic neurons into a network as versatile as the brain will be incomparably harder. The network must be staggeringly complex. Oliver Selfridge, a mathematician at M.I.T.'s Lincoln Laboratory, compares it to "pandemonium." At the lowest level is a swarm of minor "demons," representing the parts of the network that perceive such basic things as color, pitch of sound, crossings of lines, and other clues the brain uses to identify things. When the brain perceives something, the demons clamor for the attention of a foreman demon. He makes sense of their howling and, in turn, yells a summary up at a super-demon on a still higher level. This process goes on, level upon level, until the clamor reaches a master demon at the top, who is capable of integrating the whole perception.

It is doubtful whether anyone will soon try to build a computer like Selfridge's pandemonium. It would be the devil of a job.

APPENDIX

STRAIGHT LINES OF MANY SHAPES

Euclid's concept of a straight line is neither general enough nor precise enough to suit the purposes of modern mathematics. He defined a straight line as "a curve which lies evenly with the points in itself." Modern mathematicians have departed from such inscrutable descriptions. Instead they define a straight line by one of its basic properties: the fact that it is the shortest distance between two points. As a result, "straight" lines have a variety of shapes in different circumstances. It is less confusing to dispense altogether with the term "straight line" with its vague intuitive meaning and speak instead of "geodesic," precisely defined as the shortest distance between two points.

On the surface of the earth, assuming it to be a perfect sphere, the shortest distance between two points is an arc of a great circle—i.e., a circle that intersects the ends of any diameter, as meridians intersect the earth's axis at the poles. This is indeed a peculiar sort of straight line. It has no parallels, for it intersects at two points every other great circle. Moreover, it is finite, although it has no boundary. In other geometries, applicable to other sorts of surfaces, geodesics have still other properties. On a saddle-shaped surface, for example, every geodesic has an infinite number of parallels passing through a given point that does not lie on the geodesic. And all the geodesics are infinite, although there are boundaries which they continually approach without ever reaching.

The modern concept of geodesic has led physicists to speak of "curved space." In Einstein's general theory of relativity, for example, space is considered to be curved much like the surface of a sphere. At every point the extent of the curvature depends on the matter in the space. There is ample experimental evidence to justify this mathematical model of the universe. The path of starlight, which travels only along geodesics, is indeed bent when it passes near the sun.

The point is that it is difficult, perhaps impossible, to give a consistent mathematical meaning to the common intuitive notion of straightness. The idea of straightness depends entirely on personal experience with a particular universe. The diagram below, for example, shows a bug that inhabits the universe of the floor and the table leg. It knows only the path it actually crawls over, for it is blind, deaf, and unable to sense gravity. It is, however, an uncommonly wise bug in one respect: it always takes the shortest route, which it logically considers a straight line.

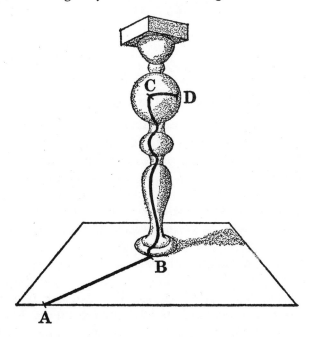

In crawling from A to B the bug's notion of a straight line corresponds to our own intuitive notion:

But from B to C the bug's straight line looks like this:

And from *C* to *D* the bug's straight line we would call the arc of a circle:

TAKE ANY NUMBER SYSTEM

It is pure convention that most of the human race does arithmetic in the decimal system. The practice of representing all numbers by combinations of just ten digits—0, 1, 2, 3, 4, 5, 6, 7, 8, and 9—originated probably because people counted on their fingers. But the properties of numbers transcend the decimal system; it is equally valid to represent numbers by combinations of any assortment of digits.

Other civilizations have indeed used other number systems. The Babylonians, for example, based their numbers on 60 digits. The Ancient Greeks (who wore open-toed sandals) used 20 digits. Even modern languages bear vestiges of non-decimal number systems. The French word for 80 is "quatre-vingt"—i.e., four times 20. English and German have special words for every whole number up to twelve, and there is perhaps a historic significance to the word "dozen."

Non-decimal number systems have some special uses even today. Computers do arithmetic mainly in the binary system, which uses only two digits, 0 and

1. The binary system is peculiarly suited to computer technology, for it is simple to manipulate 0's and 1's with switches that are either on or off or with ferrite cores that are magnetized in either of two directions. The scheme of representing numbers in binary is in principle the same as the scheme for decimal representation. In decimal, 496 stands for $4 \times 10^2 + 9 \times 10^1 + 6 \times 10^0$. (The first power of a number is the number itself; the zeroeth power is equal to 1.) Similarly, in binary, 110010 stands for $1 \times 2^5 + 1 \times 2^4 + 0 \times 2^3 + 0 \times 2^2 + 1 \times 2^1 + 0 \times 2^0$. Adding up the terms shows that this is the same number that is written as 50 in the decimal system. The rules for multiplying and adding binary numbers are remarkably simple. The multiplication table, in its entirety, is: $0 \times 0 = 0$; $0 \times 1 = 1 \times 0 = 0$; $1 \times 1 = 1$. For addition: $0 + 0 = 0$; $0 + 1 = 1 + 0 = 1$; $1 + 1 = 0$ (and carry a 1).

Any base number would work out just as well as 10 or 2. Take the base as 4, for example. In this system, the digits represent multiples of the powers of 4. Multiplication and addition would obey the rules in these tables:

Addition

	0	1	2	3
0	0	1	2	3
1	1	2	3	10
2	2	3	10	11
3	3	10	11	12

Multiplication

	0	1	2	3
0	0	0	0	0
1	0	1	2	3
2	0	2	10	12
3	0	3	12	21

Following these tables, here is an example of multiplication:

Base 4	Same numbers in Decimal—
$23102 = 2\times4^4+3\times4^3+1\times4^2+2\times4^0 =$	722
$321 = 3\times4^2+2\times4^1+1\times4^0 =$	57

$$\begin{array}{r} 23102 \\ 112210 \\ 201312 \\ \hline 22003002 \end{array} \qquad \begin{array}{r} 5054 \\ 3610 \\ \hline 41154 \end{array}$$

$22003002 = 2\times4^7+2\times4^6+3\times4^3+2\times4^0 = 41154$

It is even possible to use number systems in which the digits do not simply represent multiples of the powers of the base number. One such is the "cyclically permuted code," known as "CP." It is the binary system changed so that any two successive numbers are always the same except for one digit. This simplifies "carrying" when doing arithmetic in a computer. The formula for converting CP to decimal is somewhat more complicated. In CP the nth digit from the right represents a multiple of (2^n-1) and the 1's in a number have alternately plus and minus signs. Thus: 1011 is equivalent in decimals to $15-3+1=13$; and 11011 is equivalent to $31-15+3-1=18$; and 111011 is equivalent to $63-31+15-3+1=45$.

The higher the base, the fewer digits it takes to represent any given number. Take, for example, the year 1959. Here is how it would appear in various number systems:

Binary	Base 4	Base 7	Base 9
11110100111	132213	5466	2616

Using the base 60, you could write 1959 in only two digits. Admirably concise, but on the other hand Babylonian children had to learn 60 different symbols for digits before they could start to do arithmetic.

PATHS ON A DOUGHNUT

Geometric figures take a lot of abuse in the branch of geometry known as topology. Ordinary Euclidean geometry permits only rigid motions of figures; lengths, angles, and shapes never change. But in topology, figures can be folded, stretched, shrunk, bent, or distorted in almost any other way so long as nearby points remain close to one another. Straight lines may become curves and curves straight lines under this treatment, and such measurements as angle, length, area, and volume have no significance.

Among the few basic and unchanging geometric properties that topologists consider is "connectivity." For surfaces you can think of connectivity as the *maximum* number of cuts you can make—i.e., simple closed curves you can draw—without dividing the surface into disconnected pieces. If you draw a closed curve on a cube, for instance, you are bound to cut it in two; the same for a sphere, which is topologically equivalent to a cube. But if you draw a circle on a torus (doughnut) in the right way, it still hangs together. This demonstrates an essential difference between the connectivity of a doughnut and that of a sphere. There is another way (not shown) of slicing a doughnut so that one cut forms two pieces.

Connectivity often has surprising implications. There is an old puzzle: connect each of three houses with each of three wells by paths that do not cross. It is actually impossible to do so on a plane, a sphere, or any other surface with similar connectivity. But on a doughnut, or any other figure with a higher order of connectivity, the puzzle is simple to solve (see below).

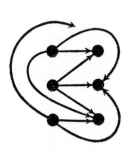 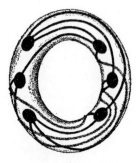

Another illustration of the basic difference between the connectivity of a sphere and that of a doughnut is the four-color theorem. It amounts to the following statement: a cartographer never needs more than four colors to make a map on which touching countries have different colors. Mathematicians have been unable to prove this theorem. But on the other hand, no one has ever drawn a map that requires five or more colors. The theorem applies only, however, to maps on surfaces with the connectivity of a sphere or a plane. On a doughnut, with its higher connectivity, the situation is entirely different. Mathematicians have been able to prove that a cartographer needs five colors for some doughnut maps but never six or more.

ALGEBRA UNDER NEW RULES

Mathematicians have emancipated many parts of modern algebra from the familiar rules of arithmetic. A prime example is matrix algebra. Matrices are rectangular blocks of numbers. In some respect the blocks behave like ordinary numbers. They can be added, subtracted, and multiplied, though not divided. But in other respects, as will be shown later, matrices do not obey the rules of arithmetic.

Matrices were invented a century ago in connection with analytic geometry, particularly to study stretching, rotation, and other simple changes and movements of geometric figures. Since then mathematicians have found ways to apply matrices to an extraordinary number of fields. Engineers use matrices to represent the distortion of a steel beam under stress, the configuration of electrical and magnetic fields, the pattern of airflow over a wing, vibrations in an engine, and many other phenomena. Physicists developed quantum theory with matrices, and a generalized form of matrix, called a tensor, is essential to relativity theory. Matrices also help solve the simultaneous differential equations that pervade the sciences.

A matrix can have any size and proportions. For simplicity's sake, however, let us start by examining the operations of matrix algebra with matrices that have only two rows and two columns. Take two matrices, A and B, written thus:

$$A = \begin{pmatrix} 0 & 1 \\ 2 & 3 \end{pmatrix} \qquad B = \begin{pmatrix} 4 & 6 \\ 5 & 7 \end{pmatrix}$$

To multiply a matrix by an ordinary number, simply multiply each "entry" within the matrix by that number:

$$5 \times A = \begin{pmatrix} 5 \times 0 & 5 \times 1 \\ 5 \times 2 & 5 \times 3 \end{pmatrix} = \begin{pmatrix} 0 & 5 \\ 10 & 15 \end{pmatrix}$$

To add two matrices, add the corresponding entries and write them in a new matrix of the same size and shape:

$$A + B = \begin{pmatrix} 0+4 & 1+6 \\ 2+5 & 3+7 \end{pmatrix} = \begin{pmatrix} 4 & 7 \\ 7 & 10 \end{pmatrix}$$

To subtract one matrix from another, subtract the corresponding entries and write a new matrix, as in addition:

$$B-A=\begin{pmatrix} 4-0 & 6-1 \\ 5-2 & 7-3 \end{pmatrix} \quad = \quad \begin{pmatrix} 4 & 5 \\ 3 & 4 \end{pmatrix}$$

Multiplying two matrices is somewhat more complicated. At the start, multiply each entry in the first *row* of A by the corresponding entry in the first *column* of B; add the results and make the number the first-row-first-column entry of a new matrix. Then multiply each entry in the second row of A by the corresponding entry in the first column of B; add the results and make the number the second-row-first-column entry of the new matrix. The other entries in the new matrix are filled in by the same procedure— i.e., the row of A determines the row position in the new matrix, and the column of B determines its column position. The complete calculation is as follows:

$$A\times B=\begin{pmatrix} 0\times4+1\times5 & 0\times6+1\times7 \\ 2\times4+3\times5 & 2\times6+3\times7 \end{pmatrix} \quad = \quad \begin{pmatrix} 5 & 7 \\ 23 & 33 \end{pmatrix}$$

Matrix multiplication does not obey the commutative law of arithmetic; it may make a difference which matrix you write first. B×A is indeed different from A×B, as this calculation shows:

$$B\times A=\begin{pmatrix} 4\times0+6\times2 & 4\times1+6\times3 \\ 5\times0+7\times2 & 5\times1+7\times3 \end{pmatrix} \quad = \quad \begin{pmatrix} 12 & 22 \\ 14 & 26 \end{pmatrix}$$

There is a matrix that corresponds to the number zero; that is, when the zero matrix is multiplied by any other matrix, the product is the zero matrix. Not surprisingly, every entry of the zero matrix is zero:

$$\begin{pmatrix} 0 & 0 \\ 0 & 0 \end{pmatrix}$$

There is also a matrix that corresponds to the number one; it does not change the value of any matrix with which it is multiplied. It is called the identity matrix, I, and is made up of 1's along the diagonal starting at the upper left-hand corner and 0's at every other entry:

$$\begin{pmatrix} 1 & 0 \\ 0 & 1 \end{pmatrix}$$

Multiplication with the identity matrix is commutative; it makes no difference which matrix is written first:

$$I \times A = \begin{pmatrix} 1\times0+0\times2 & 1\times1+0\times3 \\ 0\times0+1\times2 & 0\times1+1\times3 \end{pmatrix} = \begin{pmatrix} 0 & 1 \\ 2 & 3 \end{pmatrix}$$

$$A \times I = \begin{pmatrix} 0\times1+1\times0 & 0\times0+1\times1 \\ 2\times1+3\times0 & 2\times0+3\times1 \end{pmatrix} = \begin{pmatrix} 0 & 1 \\ 2 & 3 \end{pmatrix}$$

Matrix algebra differs from arithmetic in another important respect: the product of two matrices may be zero even though neither of them is the zero matrix. For example:

$$\begin{pmatrix} 2 & 4 \\ -1 & -2 \end{pmatrix} \times \begin{pmatrix} 0 & 2 \\ 0 & -1 \end{pmatrix} =$$

$$\begin{pmatrix} 2\times0+\ 4\times0 & 2\times2+\ 4\times-1 \\ -1\times0+-2\times0 & -1\times2+-2\times-1 \end{pmatrix} = \begin{pmatrix} 0 & 0 \\ 0 & 0 \end{pmatrix}$$

As a consequence, matrices cannot be "canceled" as ordinary numbers can be; in an equation such as $A \times C = B \times C$, A is not necessarily equal to B even if C is different from zero.

With matrices of arbitrary shapes and sizes there

are also some restrictions on adding, subtracting, and multiplying. If two matrices have exactly the same shape and size they can be added or subtracted by the same procedure that applies to 2×2 matrices. Otherwise, addition and subtraction are meaningless.

Two matrices can be multiplied together only if the first has the same number of columns as the second has rows. If this is the case, the product is a matrix with the same number of rows as the first and the same number of columns as the second. The multiplication process is essentially the same as multiplication of two 2×2 matrices:

$$\begin{pmatrix} 3 & 1 & 4 \\ 2 & 3 & 5 \end{pmatrix} \times \begin{pmatrix} 1 & 3 & 5 & 2 \\ 1 & 6 & 5 & 0 \\ 0 & 2 & 3 & 6 \end{pmatrix} =$$

$$\begin{pmatrix} 3 \times 1 + 1 \times 1 + 4 \times 0 & 3 \times 3 + 1 \times 6 + 4 \times 2 \\ 2 \times 1 + 3 \times 1 + 5 \times 0 & 2 \times 3 + 3 \times 6 + 5 \times 2 \\ 3 \times 5 + 1 \times 5 + 4 \times 3 & 3 \times 2 + 1 \times 0 + 4 \times 6 \\ 2 \times 5 + 3 \times 5 + 5 \times 3 & 2 \times 2 + 3 \times 0 + 5 \times 6 \end{pmatrix} =$$

$$\begin{pmatrix} 4 & 23 & 32 & 30 \\ 5 & 34 & 40 & 34 \end{pmatrix}$$

THE BEST OF ALL POSSIBLE . . .

A broad segment of modern applied mathematics is directly concerned with strategy and planning.

Mainly since World War II, mathematicians have developed a variety of concepts and techniques for making decisions. Earlier in this book we have outlined statistical decision theory and game theory. Now let us take a look at linear programing, a way of picking the best course of action from among an infinite number of courses.

Linear programing is an important tool in Operations Research. Military men have applied it to strategy, and an increasing number of businessmen are using it to plan a wide variety of operations. Oil companies, in particular, depend on linear programing for scheduling production, planning exploration, and systematizing pipeline and tanker transport. Food companies also rely on linear programing to plot the flow of products among plants, warehouses, and distribution points. Machine shops use linear programing to allocate men and machines to different jobs.

The mathematical concepts behind linear programing can be illustrated in the following hypothetical problem. An oil refinery wants to plan its day's production so as to maximize profit. The refinery can turn out two products: gasoline, on which the profit is $.20 per barrel, and a jet fuel blend, on which the profit is $.10 per barrel. There are a number of practical limitations—mathematicians call them "constraints." (1) Only 10,000 barrels of crude oil are available for processing. (2) The refinery must produce at least 1,000 barrels of jet fuel to satisfy a government contract. (3) It must also produce at least 2,000 barrels of gasoline to fill the immediate needs of a distributor. (4) Both products must be shipped in trucks, and only a limited number of trucks are on hand—just enough for 180,000 barrel-miles. The jet fuel is to be delivered to an airfield 10 miles from the refinery, but the gasoline must be transported 30 miles to the distributor.

Linear programing starts by expressing each of these constraints as a simple algebraic inequality. Letting x equal the barrels of jet fuel to be produced and y the barrels of gasoline, the inequalities corresponding to the constraints are:

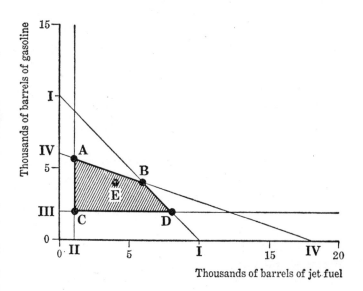

(I) $x+y \leqq 10,000$
(II) $x \geqq 1,000$
(III) $y \geqq 2,000$
(IV) $10x+30y \leqq 180,000$

The symbol $\geqq$ means "equal to or greater than," and the symbol $\leqq$ means "equal to or less than."

Each of these constraints represents a straight-line boundary on the graph below. The shaded area they fence off is made up of points that represent all the proportions of jet fuel and gasoline that the refinery could produce under the given limitations. Point E, for example, stands for 4,000 barrels of each.

The problem is to find the point of the shaded area for which the profit—$.20 \times y + $.10 \times x$—is the greatest. According to linear programing theory, the maximum (and also the minimum) profit will occur at one of the corners of the shaded area. Only the profits at four points, therefore, need be calculated.

Point	x-value	y-value	profit
A	100	$\dfrac{1{,}700}{3}$	$123.33
B	550	450	$145.06 (maximum)
C	100	200	$ 50.00 (minimum)
D	800	200	$120.00

Most real-life linear programing problems are, of course, far more complex. Each added constraint increases the number of corners. Worse yet, each added variable increases the number of dimensions of the shaded area. With only two variables—barrels of jet fuel and barrels of gasoline—the figure is a polygon. With three variables, it would be a solid geometric figure, and the constraints would be plane surfaces. With four variables, it would be a fourth-dimensional figure bounded by solid constraints.

Fortunately, mathematicians have developed methodical ways to solve linear programs without attempting to visualize multi-dimensional geometric figures. The techniques involve matrix algebra (see pages 105-109). Each constraint becomes a row in a matrix. The method in general use requires finding the inverse of the matrix—i.e., a new matrix that when multiplied by the original matrix is equal to the identity matrix. The procedure is tedious because for any sizable matrix it involves an enormous number of multiplications—e.g., 80 million of them for a matrix with 200 rows and 1,000 columns. Modern computers, however, can invert such matrices in at most a few hours.

Linear programing, on the face of it, is not much like game theory. But the two methods rest on the same mathematical foundations. In fact, it has been proved that any linear program problem can be converted to a two-person zero-sum game (in which two sides compete and one wins what the other loses); and conversely, any two-person zero-sum game can be converted to a linear program problem.

II

WHITHER THE TRAVELING SALESMAN?

Even today there are a few areas of mathematics where a gifted and persistent amateur might be able to make discoveries. One is the class of problems that mathematicians call "combinatorial." They are, by and large, easy to understand, but many of them have proved intractable. A simple and still unsolved combinatorial problem, for example, is: How many ways can you fold a strip of postage stamps? It is easy enough to work out the answer for special cases involving a few stamps. But so far no mathematician has been able to find a general rule for solving the problem for any arbitrary number of stamps.

Equally exasperating is the traveling salesman problem, with which a good many mathematicians have wrestled unsuccessfully for more than twenty years. A traveling salesman wants to start out from Washington, D.C., visit every state capital in turn, and come back to Washington. He can tell from road maps the distance between any two capitals. How should he plan his itinerary so as to make the trip as short as possible?

It would be tempting to turn the problem over to a computer, let the machine calculate the lengths of all possible trips, and then choose the shortest. But as in most combinatorial problems, there are far too many possible trips for even the fastest computer to handle. Up to 1959 the salesman, indeed, had a choice of about 3×10^{62} routes ($49 \times 48 \times 47 \times \ldots \times 3 \times 2$

of them, to be exact). If he had had a computer on each square inch of the earth, land, and sea, and if each computer could calculate the length of a billion routes per second, he would have had to wait a billion-billion-billion centuries for an answer. Meanwhile, however, Hawaii would have become the fiftieth state, and he would have to start all over again, and this time the problem would take fifty times as long.

There is still no general way to solve the traveling salesman problem for an arbitrary number of cities on any map. George Dantzig, Ray Fulkerson, and Selmer Johnson of Rand Corp., have, however, worked out a solution (*Journal of the Operations Research Society of America,* November, 1954) to the problem as it was stated before Alaska joined the Union. They used the technique called "linear programing" (see pages 110-113). If they had gone about the programing in a routine way, making a complete mathematical model of the problem at the start, the program would have been so enormous it would have taken centuries to solve. But they ingeniously refused to cross bridges until they came to them. They began with an obviously incomplete model— in effect, a rough mathematical outline of the problem, including a list of the distances between cities. (Actually, they substituted for some state capitals other cities for which road map distances were easy to look up.)

Dantzig, Fulkerson, and Johnson realized that they had not included enough constraints to define the problem. In fact, when they carried out the linear programing technique, they got a diagram like this:

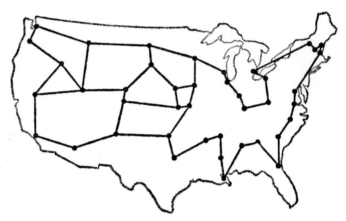

At this stage, they added a few more mathematical constraints to "break open" the loops. After that their program was able to determine the shortest route, which is:

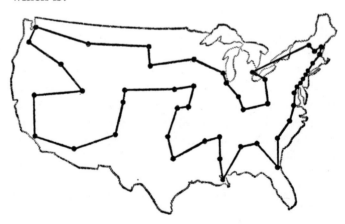

The calculation was so simple that they did not need a computer; they did all the reckoning in a few hours with paper and pencil.

THE DIFFERENT LOGICS OF CHANCE

Anyone who has studied dice knows that he will throw a given double—say, 6-6—only half as often as a given non-double—say, 5-3. It is not obvious why this is so if the two cubes are identical. But it becomes easy to see if you consider one to be red, the other green. Then there is only one way to throw a 6-6 but two distinct ways to throw a 5-3: one, 5 on the red and 3 on the green; the other, 3 on the red and 5 on the green.

The same reasoning applies to a handful of marbles tossed at random into a number of boxes. Suppose that there are 6 marbles and 3 boxes. If you consider that the marbles are distinguishable—numbered, perhaps—then there are 3^6, or 729, possible distributions of marbles among boxes. If the tossing is random and all distributions are equally probable, the probability of tossing all the marbles in the first box is 1/729. But the probability of tossing five marbles in the first box and one in the third box is 6/729, because there are six different ways of choosing a marble to put in the third box. Actual experiments along this line show that marbles do indeed behave as if they were distinguishable.

When physicists were developing statistical mechanics before the turn of the century, they assumed that particles would behave in the same way as dice or marbles. With a line of reasoning called "Maxwell-Boltzmann statistics" they treated particles as distinguishable. They thus inferred that if r particles were randomly distributed among n energy states, there would be n^r equally likely distributions (the same formula used for marbles and boxes). Unfortunately, Maxwell-Boltzmann statistics failed to produce predictions that agreed with observations and experiments.

It turned out that the logic of chance that applies to marbles and dice is out of place in the atomic realm. Particles behave as if they were *not* distinguishable. Furthermore, a different logic of chance applies to each of two groups of particles.

Bose-Einstein statistics gives accurate predictions about photons, atomic nuclei, and atoms containing an even number of elementary particles (i.e., the total number of protons, neutrons, and electrons is even). Bose-Einstein statistics is based on the assumption that particles are indistinguishable. If marbles behaved this way, the two distributions discussed above—all in the first box or five in the first and one in the third box—would be equally probable. In this system, r particles can be randomly distributed among n energy states in $\binom{n+r-1}{r}$ equally probable ways.

The expression inside the tall parentheses represents the number of different combinations of r things that can be picked from a collection of $(n+r$

−1) things. It is called the binomial coefficient and can be calculated by the following formula. If the coefficient is $\binom{a}{b}$ it is equal to $\dfrac{a!}{b!(a-b)!}$ The exclamation point indicates the "factorial" of a number —i.e., $a! = a \times (a-1) \times (a-2) \times (a-3) \times \ldots$ down to 1. For example, if in the paragraph above $n=6$ and $r=4$, then

$$\binom{n+r-1}{r} = \binom{9}{4} = \frac{9!}{4! \times 5!} =$$

$$\frac{9 \times 8 \times 7 \times 6 \times 5 \times 4 \times 3 \times 2 \times 1}{5 \times 4 \times 3 \times 2 \times 1 \times 5 \times 4 \times 3 \times 2 \times 1} = 126.$$

Still another logic of chance gives rise to Fermi-Dirac statistics, which physicists apply to particles that do not obey Bose-Einstein statistics. In Fermi-Dirac statistics the assumption is that particles are indistinguishable and that, moreover, no two particles can occupy the same energy state. There must, of course, be at least as many energy states as particles. The number of equally probable distributions is $\binom{n}{r}$. Fermi-Dirac statistics has given excellent predictions of the behavior of protons, neutrons, and electrons.

The performance of the three "statistics" points up an essential difference between mathematics and theoretical physics. From the mathematician's viewpoint, the three systems are equally logical. But the physicist is justified in using the Bose-Einstein and

Fermi-Dirac statistics simply because they accurately model the physical world. And someday physicists may have to look to mathematics for a third model to represent still other kinds of particles.

In a more frivolous application, probability theory gives a surprising answer to the following question: How many people would have to crowd into a room so that there is a better than 50-50 chance that *at least* two of them have the same birthday? In view of the fact that there are 365 possible birthdays (disregarding February 29), most people would guess the answer to be 183. But it isn't nearly so high. And here is the way to prove it by elementary probability theory.

It is easier to start by turning the problem around and calculating the probability that *no* two people in the crowd have the same birthday. If there are just two people in the room, the probability that they have different birthdays is equal to the number of combinations of different birthdays (365×364) divided by the number of possible combinations of birthdays (365×365). The same reasoning extended to an arbitrary number of people—say, n of them—produces the following formula:

$$\frac{365 \times 364 \times 363 \times \; . \; . \; . \; \times (365 - n + 1)}{365 \times 365 \times 365 \times \; . \; . \; . \; \times 365}$$

The more numbers there are in the fraction—in other words, the larger n gets—the smaller is the value of the fraction. When n is 22, the value is just a little bigger than ½; but when n is 23, it is just a little less than ½. This means that when there are 23 people in the room there is less than a 50-50 chance that no two have the same birthday. Or, turning the problem back to its original form, when as many as 23 people are in the room, you ought to bet even money that at least two have the same birthday.

THE PARADOX OF THE MIDDLE THIRDS

About the turn of the century, mathematicians began finding serious flaws in the familiar intuitive notion of dimension. A number of apparent paradoxes forced them to develop gradually the rigorous modern concepts of point-set geometry. One of the most thought-provoking point sets was suggested by the German Georg Cantor, who described it as follows:

Take a line segment one unit long and remove the middle third—i.e., all points greater than one-third but less than two-thirds the distance from one end. Note that the points at one-third and two-thirds remain. Then, similarly, remove the middle third of each of the remaining segments. Repeat this process indefinitely many times.

The geometric figure that results is indeed curious. The whole length of the original line has been removed. For the total of the removed lengths can be written as an infinite series: $1 \times 1/3 + 2 \times 1/3^2 + 2^2 \times 1/3^3$ . . . , which equals 1. Yet there remains an infinite number of unconnected points—e.g., 1/3, 2/3, 1/9, 2/9, 7/9, 8/9, 1/27, 2/27, etc. It is even theoretically possible to match these remaining points with all the points of the original line, much as you would match the fingers on your right hand with the fingers on your left hand.

Not until recent years have mathematicians had a theory of dimension that could cope with such odd geometric figures as the remaining points in Cantor's middle-thirds set. The theory amounts to applying the following test to each geometric figure. Surround each point of the figure with a very small region, such as a circle or a sphere. The number of dimensions in which the figure and region intersect is equal to one less than the number of dimensions of the figure.

An empty space has, purely by definition, a dimension of -1. Scattered points have a dimension of 0, because if you draw a small enough circle around any of them, the circle will not intersect any other point (or, so to speak, the circle will intersect the rest of the figure in -1 dimensions). A line has a dimension of 1, because if you draw a small circle around any point on the line, it will intersect the line in at least one point (0 dimension). A square has 2 dimensions, because any small circle around a point in the square intersects the square along an arc (1 dimension). A cube has 3 dimensions, because any small sphere around a point of the cube intersects the cube along a surface (2 dimensions). With similar reasoning it is possible to test figures of arbitrarily many dimensions.

What of the middle-thirds point set? It has 0 dimension, it turns out, because it is possible to surround any of the unconnected points with a small circle that will not intersect any other point in the set. The circle might, for example, have a radius equal to some fraction of π. In this case, it would pass between the points of the set.

THE CURIOUS CROSS-RATIO

All maps of the earth drawn on flat sheets of paper are grossly distorted in one way or another. Inevitably so, for the geometric properties of a sphere and a plane are basically different. The curvature of the earth is impossible to represent on a flat map, although the distortion is not serious for small areas, like those usually shown on road maps.

From the outset the mapmaker is faced with a choice of compromises. He can in general represent free from distortion either areas or angles, but never both. In the familiar Mercator projection, for example, angles on the map are precisely equal to corresponding angles on the earth. This makes the Mercator projection particularly handy for navigation, since mariners can read headings directly from the map. Polar explorers, on the other hand, have little use for the Mercator projection. It makes the Arctic and Antarctic enormous out of all proportion, and the Poles cannot even be mapped, since they are in theory projected to infinity.

The question of what properties, such as angle or area, are reproduced on a map without distortion is of prime interest to mathematicians. The question extends far beyond the confines of geometry, for all mathematics can be considered broadly as a study of maps and mapping. For all their bewildering equations and terminology, what theoretical physicists are actually doing is making mathematical maps of the physical world. Mathematicians, for their part, apply mapping to algebra and other fields as well as geometry. In so doing they often study transformations in terms of the properties of figures and formulas that remain unchanged, or "invariant."

In ordinary Euclidean geometry, for example, the invariants are all those properties that are unchanged by motions of rigid bodies—e.g., lengths, areas, volumes, curvature. Projective geometry is defined by many fewer invariants. A straight line is projected into a straight line; a point into a point. Curved lines are generally projected into curved lines, although their shape may be changed; a circle, for example, may be transformed into an ellipse.

The projective transformation shown in the diagram below distorts distances. (The line in the upper plane is projected onto the line in the lower plane from a point, not shown in the picture, which is the intersection of the four lines AA', BB', CC', and DD'.)

Even the ratios between two distances or among three distances may change. But among four points on a line there is a relationship of distances that is invariant in a curious and complex fashion. Consider the line in the top plane through the points A, B, C, and D and its projection in the bottom plane through the points A', B', C', and D'. Then calculate the "cross-ratio" of the internal parts of the line $ABCD$ according to this formula: $\dfrac{AC}{BC} \div \dfrac{AD}{BD}$. This cross-ratio can be any number, but it is always equal to the corsponding cross-ratio for $A'B'C'D'$—i.e: $\dfrac{A'C'}{B'C'} \div \dfrac{A'D'}{B'D'}$.

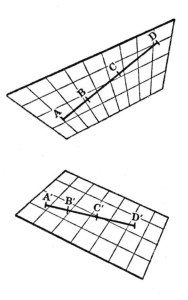

This cross-ratio invariance is utterly independent of the arrangement of the points on the lines. You might, for example, change the order of the letters so that the top line was:

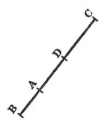

and the bottom line was:

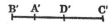

In that case the cross-ratios, calculated according to the original formula, would have a different numerical value, but they would still be equal. There are, in fact, twenty-four ways to arrange the order of the four letters, but no matter how they are arranged the cross-ratios are equal.

A more general sort of invariance, also in the realm of projective geometry, is expressed in a famous theorem of Blaise Pascal, a seventeenth century French mathematician. Pascal discovered it while in his teens. The theorem applies to conic sections: the curves formed by the intersections of a hollow right circular cone and planes that cut through it at various angles. A cone is intimately related to a circle, which is the intersection of a cone and any plane perpendicular to the axis of the cone. By cutting a cone at other angles you can make the other conic sections— ellipse, hyperbola, parabola, even a pair of straight lines.

Pascal's theorem says that if you inscribe in any conic section a hexagon of any proportions, the opposite sides of the hexagon (extended as far as necessary) intersect in three points that lie along a straight line. If the conic section is a circle and the hexagon is fairly regular, the opposite sides intersect quite a distance away.

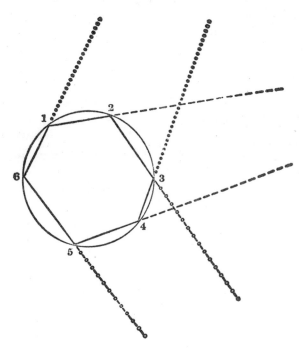

It is easier to see what Pascal meant if you choose an ellipse and inscribe a hexagon that crisscrosses. There's no law that says a hexagon can't crisscross, but you have to keep track of "opposite" sides by the numbers on the corners. (In this diagram, sides 1-2 and 5-6 don't have to be extended; they intersect inside the hexagon.)

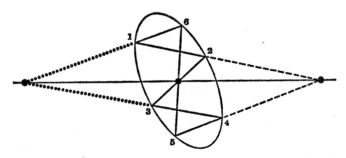

Interestingly, Greek mathematicians who lived in Alexandria during the Roman era knew that this theorem was true in a special case—i.e., when the conic section was a pair of intersecting straight lines. Pascal's theorem illustrates the kind of generalization that mathematicians find particularly beautiful.